Merrill Spelling

CENTENNIAL EDITION
100 YEARS
MERRILL SPELLING

About the Authors

Dr. Gillian E. Cook is Associate Professor of Supervision and Elementary Education at the University of Texas at San Antonio. She received her B.A. from Sir George Williams University in Montreal and her Ed.M. and Ed.D. from Harvard University. Dr. Cook has extensive teaching experience at all grade levels and has served as a consultant to many school systems in the United States, Canada, and Great Britain.

Dr. Marisa Esposito is currently an Associate Examiner at Educational Testing Services in Princeton, New Jersey. Previously she was an Assistant Professor of English at Newark College of Arts and Sciences at Rutgers University in Newark, New Jersey. She received her B.A., her M.A., and her Ph.D. in English from Kent State University, Kent, Ohio. Dr. Esposito has extensive teaching and publishing experience.

Terry R. Gabrielson is an Elementary School Principal at Fairview School in Blytheville, Arkansas. He received his B.S. in Elementary Education and his M.S. in Elementary School Administration from St. Cloud State University, St. Cloud, Minnesota. He has been a curriculum coordinator and an elementary teacher and has served in numerous consulting roles to parents, teachers, administrators, and textbook publishers.

Dr. Jean Wallace Gillet is Assistant Professor of Education at the University of Virginia. She received her B.A. from Western Michigan University, her M.A.T. from Oakland University in Rochester, Michigan, and her Ed.D. from the University of Virginia. She has extensive teaching experience. She is also coauthor of *Language Arts* and *Understanding Reading Problems*.

Dr. Charles Temple is Department Chair and Associate Professor of Education at Hobart and William Smith Colleges in Geneva, New York. He received his B.A. in English from the University of North Carolina and his M.Ed. and Ph.D. in Education from the University of Virginia. He has been a high school English teacher, reading programs director, and was a Fulbright Scholar in Portugal. In addition, he is coauthor of *Language Arts, Understanding Reading Problems, The Beginnings of Writing,* and *An Elementary Teacher's Guide to Process Writing*.

George R. Turner, Professor of English at Norwich University in Northfield, Vermont, received his B.A. from Dartmouth College and his M.Ed. from Massachusetts State College at Fitchburg. He has more than twenty years of teaching experience. Mr. Turner is a coauthor of *Common Words,* a Merrill high school spelling series.

MERRILL
PUBLISHING COMPANY
Columbus, Ohio

Editorial Review Board

Photo Credits

5, Lawrence Migdale; 36, Stock Concepts; 74, Lynn Stone; 76, Focus on Sports; 88, © Caroline Brown 1988/Fran Heyl & Assoc.; 102, Tim Courlas; 122, Ted Rice; 138, Tim Courlas; 148, Leonard Lee Rue, III/Photo Researchers; 152, Ted Rice; 155, Movie Still Archives/Copyright 1939 Loew's Incorporated. Ren. 1966 Metro-Goldwyn-Mayer Inc.; 159, Henryk J. Kaiser/Leo deWys, Inc.; 165, John D. Pearce; 174, Dennis de Cicco; 175, Aaron Haupt; 206, Bob Curtis/Light Images; 208, Alvin Staffan; 210, Animals Animals/© E.R. Degginger; 212, Stephen J. Krasemann/Photo Researchers; 214, Animals Animals/Breck P. Kent; 215, John Shaw/Tom Stack & Assoc.; 216, Animals Animals/Ted Levin; 218, 219, Pictures Unlimited; 220, Leo deWys, Inc.; 223, Light Source; 225, Image Workshop; 227, Alvin Staffan; 228, Pictures Unlimited; 231, Jeff Clark; 233, Cobalt Productions; 234, Focus on Sports.

Editorial and Production Staff

Series Editor: Beverlee Ruth Rubin Jobrack; *Editor:* Barbara C. Thompson; *Designers:* Patricia Cohan, Kip M. Frankenberry; *Art Project Coordinator:* Shirley J. Beltz; *Artist:* Sam MacKenzie-Crane; *Illustrators:* Paul Harvey, Anna Pomaska, Carol Byer, Susan Hall; *Photo Editor:* Ruth E. Bogart; *Production Project Coordinator:* Linda Peterson; *Production Editor:* Joy E. Dickerson

Cover Designer: Kate Gorman; *Cover Illustrator:* Krosnick Studios, Edgewater, NJ; *Cover Photographer:* Michael Chan

Handwriting models in this book are reproduced with permission of Zaner-Bloser, Inc., © 1989.

ISBN-0-675-02325-4

Published by

MERRILL PUBLISHING CO.

Columbus, Ohio 43216

Copyright 1990 by Merrill Publishing Co.
Formerly *Merrill Spelling for Word Mastery* © 1987, 1984

Word Study Steps

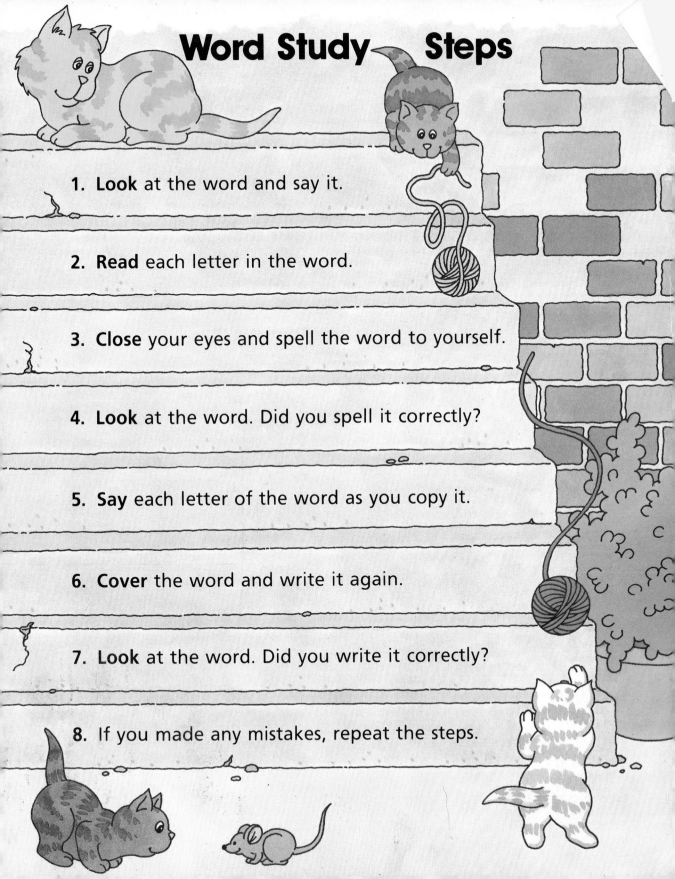

1. **Look** at the word and say it.

2. **Read** each letter in the word.

3. **Close** your eyes and spell the word to yourself.

4. **Look** at the word. Did you spell it correctly?

5. **Say** each letter of the word as you copy it.

6. **Cover** the word and write it again.

7. **Look** at the word. Did you write it correctly?

8. If you made any mistakes, repeat the steps.

CONTENTS

1

1. as
2. ant
3. fat
4. ask
5. tag
6. band
7. fast
8. class
9. land
10. have

This Week's Words

Say each spelling word. Each word has the short-**a** sound. The sign for the short-**a** sound is /a/.

The short-**a** sound can be spelled **a**.

apple   **hat**

Other Words

Write any words you and your teacher would like to add to this week's list.

—— —— ——

2

Pattern Power

Say each spelling word.

A. Write the words that begin with /a/ spelled **a.**

____

____

____

B. Write the other words in which /a/ is spelled **a.**

____ ____

____ ____

____ ____

In most words, /a/ is spelled **a.**

as
ant
fat
ask
tag
band
fast
class
land
have

Meaning Mastery

Use spelling words to complete these sentences.
The first one is done for you.

1. Our __class__ went on a picnic.

2. I saw an ___ carry a piece of cookie.

3. The cookie was almost ___ big as the ant.

4. The ant went very ___ .

5. I ___ not seen an ant since then.

6. We will ___ our teacher to go again.

Dictionary Skills

Some letters are missing from the alphabet below. Write the missing letters.

a b c d __ f g __ i j k __ m
n o __ q r s __ u v __ x y z

Word Building

Rhyming words have the same middle and ending sounds. The words **cat** and **sat** are rhyming words. Change the first letter of each word below to the letter next to the word. Write the rhyming word. The first one is done for you.

1. fat   **b** <u>at</u>

2. sand   **l** ___

3. hand   **b** ___

4. bag   **t** ___

Writing Activities

The word **I** stands for you and your name. It is always written with a capital letter. Answer these questions with a sentence about yourself. Use the word **I** to start each sentence. A **sentence** tells a complete thought. A sentence always begins with a capital letter and often ends with a period.

1. Who are you?

2. How old are you?

Handwriting Practice

Practice your handwriting. Write this sentence.

A fat cat came to our class.

Review Words

man
has
and

A. Write the review word that begins with /a/.

———

B. Write the review words that have /a/ in the middle.

———   ———

Challenge Words: Science

pond
snail
bay
stone
sand

A. Write the science words that name bodies of water.

———   ———

B. Write the science word that names something that is alive.

———

C. Write the science words that name things you could find on the beach.

———   ———

Words With Short e

This Week's Words

Say each spelling word. Each word has the short-**e** sound. The sign for the short-**e** sound is /e/.

The short-**e** sound can be spelled **e**.

ever   r**e**d

Other Words

Write any words you and your teacher would like to add to this week's list.

— — — —

1. bed
2. desk
3. end
4. every
5. wet
6. men
7. tent
8. tell
9. said
10. any

bed
desk
end
every
wet
men
tent
tell
said
any

Pattern Power

Say each spelling word.

A. Write the words that begin with /e/ spelled **e.**

—— ——

B. Write the other words in which /e/ is spelled **e.**

—— ——

—— ——

—— ——

C. Write the words in which /e/ is spelled a different way.

—— ——

In most words, /e/ is spelled **e.**

8

Meaning Mastery

Use spelling words to complete the rhyme below.

I did not want to go to (1)____ .

"I'll count to ten," my mother (2)____ .

I did not wait until the (3)____ .

I ran before she got through many.

I know next time she won't say (4)____ .

Dictionary Skills

Learn the alphabet well. It will help you find words in the dictionary faster. Write the letters that come before and after each letter below. The first one is done for you.

1. <u>d</u> e <u>f</u>   5. ___ g ___   9. ___ o ___

2. ___ q ___   6. ___ n ___   10. ___ h ___

3. ___ c ___   7. ___ w ___   11. ___ k ___

4. ___ r ___   8. ___ i ___   12. ___ b ___

bed
desk
end
every
wet
men
tent
tell
said
any

Word Building

The letters **a, e, i, o, u**, and sometimes **y** are called **vowels.** All the other letters are called **consonants.** Every word has at least one vowel. Change the vowel in each word below to **e** to make a new word. The first one is done for you.

1. and end
2. man ___
3. tall ___
4. bad ___

Writing Activities

Look at these names: **Steve, Karen, Bill.** All names of people and pets begin with capital letters. Look at the cover of your spelling book. Think of names for the animals. Write each sentence below using the names you picked.

1. The frog named ___ gets wet every day.
2. The butterfly named ___ likes to play tag.
3. The cat named ___ was on my desk.

10

Handwriting Practice

Practice your handwriting. Write this sentence.

Tim can make a paper tent.

Review Words

Write the review words that rhyme with the words below.

1. set ___ ___
2. peg ___

Challenge Words: Math

Write the math words to complete this paragraph.

A paper (1)___ is (2)___ on one end and

pointed on the other. If you (3)___ it to the right

or (4)___ it will change its (5)___ .

3

Words With Short i

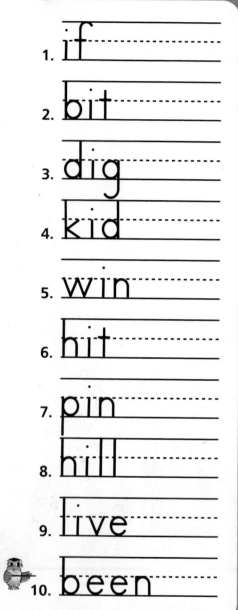

1. if
2. bit
3. dig
4. kid
5. win
6. hit
7. pin
8. hill
9. live
10. been

This Week's Words

Say each spelling word. Each word has the short-i sound. The sign for the short-i sound is /i/.

The short-i sound can be spelled i.

in   **swim**

Other Words

Write any words you and your teacher would like to add to this week's list.

_____ _____ _____ _____

Pattern Power

Say each spelling word.

1. Write the word that begins with /i/ spelled **i**.

   ___

2. Write the other words in which /i/ is spelled **i**.

   ___   ___   ___   ___

   ___   ___   ___   ___

3. Write the word in which /i/ is spelled a different way.

   ___

In most words, /i/ is spelled **i**.

if

bit

dig

kid

win

hit

pin

hill

live

been

Meaning Mastery

Write the word in each group below that goes with the word in dark print. The first one is done for you.

1. **bite**   bit   been   _bit_
2. **life**   if   live   ___
3. **dug**   kid   dig   ___
4. **be**   been   bit   ___
5. **mountain**   hill   will   ___
6. **children**   kid   hill   ___

Dictionary Skills

Write each group of letters in alphabetical order. The first one is done for you.

1. d b a c   _abcd_   4. t r s q   ___
2. j h i k   ___   5. u x w v   ___
3. n l o m   ___

Word Building

Change the vowel in each word below to the one next to the word. Write the new word. The first one is done for you.

1. if   **o** of
2. pen **i** ___
3. dig **o** ___
4. bat **i** ___
5. win **o** ___
6. hot **i** ___

Writing Activities

There are seven days in a week. They are **Sunday, Monday, Tuesday, Wednesday, Thursday, Friday,** and **Saturday.** They all start with capital letters. Write each sentence below. Start the name of each day of the week with a capital letter.

1. I will do the dishes on monday.

2. Jean and I will play outside on tuesday if it doesn't rain.

Proofreading Practice

When you proofread, draw three lines under a letter that needs to be capitalized. Make the changes shown below. Write the sentence correctly.

If <u>k</u>im plays, we will win on <u>m</u>onday.

Review Words

did
in
sit

Write the review words that rhyme with the words below.

1. bit ____   3. lid ____
2. pin ____

Challenge Words: Social Studies

library
news
television
radio
film

Use the social studies words to complete these sentences.

1. I can read the ____ in a newspaper.

2. I can watch the news on ____ .

3. I can often see a special news ____ on T.V.

4. I can listen to the news on the ____ .

5. I can read the newspaper in the ____ .

16

Words With Short o

This Week's Words

Say each spelling word. Each word has the short-**o** sound. The sign for the short-**o** sound is /o/.

The short-**o** sound can be spelled **o**.

fox   **not**

1. hot
2. doll
3. hop
4. box
5. pot
6. mop
7. top
8. rob
9. lot
10. rock

Other Words

Write any words you and your teacher would like to add to this week's list.

___ ___ ___ ___

17

hot
doll
hop
box
pot
mop
top
rob
lot
rock

Pattern Power

Say each spelling word.

A. Write the words ending in **p** in which /o/ is spelled **o.**

___ ___ ___

B. Write the words ending in **t** in which /o/ is spelled **o.**

___ ___ ___

C. Write the other words in which /o/ is spelled **o.**

___ ___ ___ ___

In most words, /o/ is spelled **o.**

Meaning Mastery

Write the spelling words that have the meanings below.

1. a large number   ___

2. very warm   ___

3. to steal   ___

4. a toy that spins   ___

5. to move by taking small jumps ___

Dictionary Skills

Write each group of letters in alphabetical order.

1. j g i f h   ___   4. a c e b d   ___

2. q r t s p   ___   5. k o m n l   ___

3. y u v w x   ___

hot
doll
hop
box
pot
mop
top
rob
lot
rock

Word Building

A **noun** names a person, place, thing, or idea. A **plural noun** is more than one person, place, thing, or idea. You usually make a noun mean "more than one" by adding **-s** to the end of the word.

Add **-s** to each noun below to make it plural. Write the new word. The first one is done for you.

1. doll   **dolls**   3. mop   ___

2. rock   ___   4. pot   ___

Writing Activities

PREPARE: What did you do last week? What did you do at school and at home?

WRITE: Write the days of the week. Then write a sentence about what you did each day. Write as many things as you can think of. Don't worry about your spelling.

REVISE: Read your writing. Are the days of the week in the right order? Did you write something for each day? Proofread for spelling and capital letters. Then copy your paper in your best handwriting. Show it to your teacher.

Proofreading Practice

This editing mark ⊙ shows that a period needs to be added. Make the changes shown by the editing marks. Then write the sentence correctly.

On monday i had to hop on the box⊙

Review Words

Write the review words that rhyme with the words below.

1. hot ___ ___
2. top ___

got
shop
not

Challenge Words: Science

Use the science words to complete this story.

Long ago, Ben Franklin flew a (1)___

during the (2)___ . The sky was dark, and

there was little (3)___ . Ben's kite flew

through the (4)___ . A sudden

(5)___ flash taught Ben about lightning.

air
daytime
kite
electric
sunlight

5 Words With Short u

1. cut
2. must
3. much
4. dug
5. rug
6. truck
7. under
8. mud
9. tub
10. some

This Week's Words

Say each spelling word. Each word has the short-u sound. The sign for the short-u sound is /u/.

The short-u sound can be spelled **u**.

run   **up**

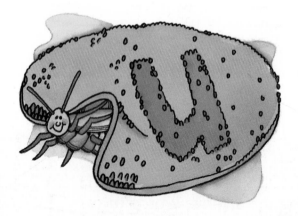

Other Words

Write any words you and your teacher would like to add to this week's list.

___ ___ ___ ___

22

Pattern Power

Say each spelling word.

A. Write the word that begins with /u/ spelled **u**.

———

B. Write the three-letter words in which /u/ is spelled **u**.

——— ——— ——— ——— ———

C. Write the four-letter words in which /u/ is spelled **u**.

——— ———

D. Write the word that ends with **ck** in which /u/ is spelled **u**.

———

E. Write the word in which /u/ is spelled a different way.

———

In most words, /u/ is spelled **u**.

cut
must
much
dug
rug
truck
under
mud
tub
some

Meaning Mastery

A **riddle** is a funny question or sentence that makes you think about what words mean. Write a spelling word to complete each riddle below. The last two words in each answer should rhyme. The first one is done for you.

1. What would an ant have on its floor?
   A bug _rug_ .

2. What do chickens ride in?
   A cluck ____ .

3. What does a baby bear take a bath in?
   A cub ____ .

Dictionary Skills

Look at the first letter in each word to alphabetize each list.

under   1. ____   must   1. ____
much   2. ____   some   2. ____
dug   3. ____   cut   3. ____

24

Word Building

Add **-s** to each word below to make it plural.

1. cut ____
2. rug ____
3. tub ____
4. truck ____
5. rock ____
6. doll ____
7. bed ____
8. ant ____

Writing Activities

PREPARE: Think about a time you were at the beach or on a vacation. Who were you with? What did you do?

WRITE: Write some sentences about your vacation or time at the beach. Write as much as you can remember. Don't worry about making mistakes. You can fix them later.

REVISE: Read your sentences. Is there anything you want to add or take out? Are your words spelled correctly? Do all your sentences start with a capital letter and end with a period? Copy your sentences neatly. Share them with a friend.

Handwriting Practice

Practice your handwriting. Write this sentence.

There is some mud under the water.

Review Words

of
fun
us

Write the review words that rhyme with the words below.

1. bus ___   3. love ___
2. run ___

Challenge Words: Math

clock
minute
moment
month
second

A. Write these math words in order from the shortest time to the longest time.

month	second	minute

1. ___   2. ___   3. ___

B. Write the math words that match these meanings.

1. it tells time ___
2. a short period of time ___

26

Review

Pattern Power

Lesson 1

Write the words with /a/ spelled these ways.

1. a ___ ___ ___
2. a-consonant-e ___

ant
ask
class
have

Lesson 2

Write the words with /e/ spelled these ways.

1. e ___ ___ ___
2. a ___

bed
every
tent
any

Lesson 3

Write the words with /i/ spelled these ways.

1. i ___ ___ ___
2. ee ___

kid
win
live
been

Lesson 4

Write the short-**o** words that rhyme with the words below.

1. hot ___   3. lock ___
2. fox ___   4. ball ___

doll
box
lot
rock

cut
much
under
some

Write the words with /u/ spelled these ways.

1. u ___ ___ ___
2. o-consonant-e ___

Meaning Mastery

A. Use review words to finish these riddles. The last two words in each answer should rhyme.

1. What can you put stones in?
   A rocks ___ .

2. What would you call a crack in a peanut?
   A nut ___ .

B. Use review words to complete this paragraph.

I have never (1)___ to the circus. But I see it on television (2)___ year. This year we (3)___ the tickets to go. I can't wait!

Word Building

ant
ask
bed
every
kid
win
doll
box
cut
much
class
have
tent
any
live
been
lot
rock
under
some

A. Write spelling words that rhyme with these words.

1. red ___   4. gum ___
2. such ___   5. pin ___
3. went ___   6. ball ___

B. Change the first letter in each word below to the one next to the word. Write the spelling word.

1. not l ___   3. sent t ___
2. give l ___   4. lid k ___

C. Write the words that are made by adding these consonants to the word parts. The first set has been done.

1. h⎫
   d⎬ot
   l⎭

2. r⎫
   b⎬ed
   f⎭

3. n⎫
   c⎬ut
   b⎭

hot ___ ___

dot ___ ___

lot ___ ___

ant
ask
bed
every
kid
win
doll
box
cut
much
class
have
tent
any
live
been
lot
rock
under
some

Dictionary Skills

A. Write the missing letters in these parts of the alphabet.

1. ab ___ d   2. ___ ghi   3. lmn ___

B. In each group, write the letter that comes first in the alphabet.

1. ced ___   2. rqs ___   3. fbm ___

C. Write the word in each pair that would come first in alphabetical order.

1. have   2. much
   ant   ___   doll   ___

Review Roundup

Write the missing letters to complete the spelling words in this puzzle.

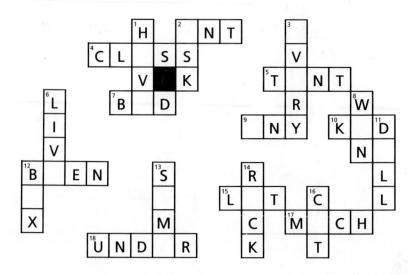

30

Spelling and Reading

A diary is a book in which you write about yourself. You can write about your feelings or things that happen to you.

Read the page below. It is from Lynn's diary.

Today was my first day of second grade. Mom said that I had to get out of bed early this morning. I was afraid. I did not feel like eating, but Mom said I had to eat something.

When we got to school, I did not want to go into the room. The teacher said, ''Come on in! Welcome to the class. My name is Miss Green.'' She looked so nice. I wasn't afraid anymore.

I had a great first day. I made a lot of friends. I like my teacher very much. I am glad to be back in school.

Answer the questions below.

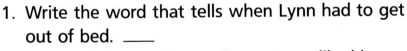

1. Write the word that tells when Lynn had to get out of bed. _____
2. Write a sentence that tells you Lynn liked her teacher.

The Writing Process

Prepare

Think of your first day of school this year. Draw a picture of one thing you did before school started in the morning. Then draw a picture of something that happened to you during the first day of school. Last, draw a picture of something you did after the first day of school.

Write

Look at your pictures. For each one, write a sentence that tells what happened. Then write a sentence that tells how you felt at the time. Do not worry about making mistakes. You can fix them later.

Revise

Read your sentences. Are they in the right order of when they happened on the first day of school? Number them to show the right order. Then check each sentence. Does it begin with a capital letter? Does it end with a period? Are your words spelled correctly? If you made a mistake, use editing marks to change it. Now copy your sentences neatly. Show them to your teacher.

EDITING MARKS

 indent or start a new paragraph

= use capital letter

 check spelling

 add letters or words

 take out

 add a period

Words With th and wh

This Week's Words

Say each spelling word. Each word begins with **th** or **wh**.
The word **this** begins with **th**. The sign for the **th** sound is /Ŧh/.

th**is**

The word **think** begins with /th/ spelled **th**.

th**ink**

The word **whale** begins with **wh**. The sign for the **wh** sound is /hw/.

wh**ale**

The word **who** begins with **wh**. The sign for this **wh** sound is /h/.

wh**o**

Other Words

Write any words you and your teacher would like to add to this week's list.

___ ___ ___

1. their
2. then
3. these
4. thank
5. whole
6. than
7. whistle
8. third
9. thing
10. those

their
then
these
thank
whole
than
whistle
third
thing
those

Pattern Power

Say each spelling word.

A. Write the words that begin with /Ŧh/ spelled **th.**

___ ___ ___ ___ ___

B. Write the words that begin with /th/ spelled **th.**

___ ___ ___

C. Write the word that begins with /hw/ spelled **wh.**

___

D. Write the word that begins with /h/ spelled **wh.**

___

In many words, /Ŧh/, as in **this,** and /th/, as in **think,** are spelled **th.** In many words, /hw/, as in **whale,** is spelled **wh.** In some words, /h/, as in **who,** is spelled **wh.**

Meaning Mastery

Use spelling words to complete this paragraph.

(1)___ are my sister's toys. She blows this (2)___ when she plays

with her trains. About the (3)___ time she blows it, Dad asks her to

stop. (4)___ it is quiet again.

Dictionary Skills

Two of the lists below are in alphabetical order. One list is not. Find
that list and write the words in alphabetical order.

A. men
thank
why

B. stop
that
where

C. whole
their
run

their
then
these
thank
whole
than
whistle
third
thing
those

Word Building

Write the spelling words that rhyme with the words below.

1. sing   ——

2. ten   ——

3. please   ——

4. bank   ——

5. bird   ——

Writing Activities

There are twelve months in a year. The names of the months begin with capital letters. Look at the names of the months below. Some need capital letters. Write the months correctly.

January	February	march	April	May	june
july	August	september	October	november	december

——   ——   ——   ——   ——

36

Proofreading Practice

Good proofreaders circle a misspelled word. Look at the editing marks in the sentences below. Write each misspelled word correctly.

1. Your ball is larger (thane) mine. ____

2. All of (thoze) books belong to Jeff. ____

Review Words

Write the review words that begin with these letters.

1. **th** ____ ____
2. **wh** ____

there
why
this

Challenge Words: Social Studies

Use the social studies words in these sentences.

1. The oldest ____ is written on a stone.
2. It is important to stay in your ____ while driving on a ____ .
3. The Concorde is a fast ____ airplane.
4. ____ is faster than traveling by bus.

map
jet
road
flying
lane

Words With ch and sh

1. chair
2. short
3. change
4. shot
5. shall
6. chew
7. chill
8. chase
9. shiny
10. shoe

This Week's Words

Say each spelling word. Each word begins with **ch** or **sh**. The sign for the **ch** sound is /ch/. The sign for the **sh** sound is /sh/.

The word **chicken** begins with /ch/ spelled **ch.**

chicken

The word **sheep** begins with /sh/ spelled **sh.**

sheep

Other Words

Write any words you and your teacher would like to add to this week's list.

___ ___ ___ ___

Pattern Power

Say each spelling word.

A. Write the words that begin with /ch/ spelled **ch.**

___ ___ ___ ___ ___

B. Write the words that begin with /sh/ spelled **sh.**

___ ___ ___ ___

In many words, /ch/ is spelled **ch.** In many words, /sh/ is spelled **sh.**

chair
short
change
shot
shall
chew
chill
chase
shiny
shoe

Meaning Mastery

Use spelling words to complete this paragraph.

Our new puppy sleeps under a (1)＿＿ in the

kitchen. He is getting new teeth and likes to

(2)＿＿ on things. We gave him an old (3)＿＿ to

chew on. We bought him a (4)＿＿ new collar. He

likes to (5)＿＿ the cat.

Dictionary Skills

Write the words below in alphabetical order.

shall   end   bug   did   chill

Word Building

A **base word** is the main part of a word. Add **-s** to each base word below. Write the new word.

1. chair ____
2. shoe ____
3. shot ____
4. change ____

Writing Activities

PREPARE: There are four seasons in a year. They are summer, fall, winter, and spring. Choose a month from each of the seasons. Think about what the weather is often like in each month. In some places, March is windy and August is hot.

WRITE: Write a sentence that tells something about the weather for each month. You may want to use the spelling words for ideas.

REVISE: Read your sentences. Did you clearly tell what the weather is like? Did you begin each month with a capital letter? Check for correct spelling. Use editing marks to show where you need to make changes. Copy your sentences in your best handwriting. Trade your sentences with a friend.

Handwriting Practice

Practice your handwriting. Write this sentence.

February is a short month.

Review Words

chin
sheep
show

Write the review words that rhyme with the words below.

1. pin   ___   3. snow   ___
2. deep   ___

Challenge Words: Science

lips
face
head
eye
ear

A. Write the science word that goes with each word below.

1. hear   ___
2. see   ___
3. think   ___
4. speak   ___

B. Write the science word that names the front part of the head. ___

Words With wh, kn, wr

This Week's Words

Say each spelling word. Each word begins with **wh, kn,** or **wr.** The word **where** begins with **wh.** The sign for the **wh** sound is /hw/.

where

The word **knock** begins with the sound /n/, spelled **kn.** It has a silent **k.**

knock

The word **wrong** begins with the sound /r/, spelled **wr.** It has a silent **w.**

wrong

Other Words

Write any words you and your teacher would like to add to this week's list.

—— —— —— ——

1. which
2. while
3. know
4. knew
5. write
6. knock
7. wheel
8. wrote
9. whenever
10. wrong

43

which
while
know
knew
write
knock
wheel
wrote
whenever
wrong

Pattern Power

Say each spelling word.

A. Write the words that begin with /hw/ spelled **wh.**

___ ___ ___ ___

B. Write the words that begin with /n/ spelled **kn.**

___ ___ ___

C. Write the words that begin with /r/ spelled **wr.**

___ ___ ___

In many words, /hw/ is spelled **wh.** In some words, /n/ is spelled **kn.** In some words, /r/ is spelled **wr.**

Meaning Mastery

Some words sound alike but have different spellings and meanings.
Look at these words: **flower**   **flour.**
A **flower** is a plant. **Flour** is used for cooking.

A. Write the spelling word that sounds like each word below. The
first one is done for you.

1. new **knew**   3. no ___
2. right ___

B. Use spelling words to complete these sentences.

1. I heard the sound of a ___ on the door.
2. A truck had lost a ___ .

Dictionary Skills

The words **cat, coat,** and **cry** begin with the same letter. To put
words like this in alphabetical order, you must look at the second
letter. Write these words in alphabetical order.

A. which 1. ___   **B.** wrote 1. ___
write 2. ___   water 2. ___
well 3. ___   while 3. ___
will 4. ___   word 4. ___

which
while
know
knew
write
knock
wheel
wrote
whenever
wrong

Word Building

A. Change the vowel in each word to the one next to the word. Write the new word.

1. write   **o** ____
2. know   **e** ____
3. whale   **i** ____

B. Use the words **write** or **wrote** in each sentence.

1. When did you ____ to James?

2. I ____ to him when we moved.

Writing Activities

Write these words in alphabetical order. They will make a sentence. Be sure the sentence starts with a capital letter and ends with a period.

is boy yellow a painting wheel the

Proofreading Practice

The proofreading mark ∧ shows where a word or letter is to be added. Make the changes shown by the editing marks below. Then write the sentences correctly.

1. I like to go swimming ∧ it is hot.

whenever

2. I don't care whi∧h pool we go to.

c

3. As long as it's a pool, we can't go.∧

wrong

Review Words

Write the review words that rhyme with these words.

1. there ____   3. then ____
2. cut ____

what
where
when

Challenge Words: Math

We work with numbers every day. Write the math word for each number below.

1. 30 ____   4. 20 ____
2. 100 ____   5. 50 ____
3. 60 ____

hundred
sixty
twenty
thirty
fifty

47

10 Consonant Clusters

1. blew
2. clap
3. blow
4. slip
5. slid
6. blind
7. clean
8. glad
9. slide
10. plant

This Week's Words

Say each spelling word. Each word begins with two consonant sounds blended together. Notice how each word begins.

blue   **glad**

play   **slow**

clown

Other Words

Write any words you and your teacher would like to add to this week's list.

___ ___ ___ ___

48

Pattern Power

Say each spelling word.

A. Write the words that begin with the letters below.

bl   ___   ___   ___

sl   ___   ___   ___

cl   ___   ___

gl   ___

pl   ___

B. What letter is the same in all the words? _____

Two consonant sounds blended together and spelled with two letters is called a **consonant cluster.**

49

blew
clap
blow
slip
slid
blind
clean
glad
slide
plant

Meaning Mastery

Write the word in each group below that goes with the word in dark print.

1. **blew**   blue   blow   ____

2. **dirty**   clean   clap   ____

3. **happy**   glad   plant   ____

4. **hands**   blow   clap   ____

5. **grow**   plant   blind   ____

Dictionary Skills

Write the words in each group in alphabetical order.

A. blew   1. ____   **B.** clean   1. ____
   slide   2. ____   plant   2. ____
   clap   3. ____   blind   3. ____
   glad   4. ____   slip   4. ____

Word Building

Change the first two letters of each word below to the letter next to the word. Write the new word. The first one is done for you.

1. slip   r   rip
2. slide   h ____
3. place   r ____
4. blind   k ____
5. glad   h ____
6. clap   m ____

Writing Activities

A **verb** is a certain kind of word. Many verbs show action. They tell something you can do. **Walk** and **sing** are verbs.

blew	clap	blow	slip	slid	clean	slide	plant

PREPARE: Look at the spelling words in the box. Think about how you could use these verbs to describe something you might do on a cold winter day.

WRITE: Write an interesting sentence for each word.

REVISE: Check each sentence for correct spelling. Check for capital letters and punctuation.

Handwriting Practice

Practice your handwriting. Write this sentence.

We slid down the slide.

Review Words

fly **play** **sleep**	Write the review words that begin with these letters. 1. **pl** ___ 3. **fl** ___ 2. **sl** ___

Challenge Words: Social Studies

baby-sitter
family
aunt
grandchildren
stepfather

Use these social studies words to complete the sentences below.

1. There are five children in my ___ .
2. My baby sister has a ___ during the day.
3. My mom's sister, my ___ , lives in Maine.
4. My grandparents have seven ___ .
5. My ___ married my mother five years ago.

Consonant Clusters

This Week's Words

Say each spelling word. Each word begins with two consonant sounds blended together. Notice how each word begins.

brown   **dr**ive

frog   **gr**een

prize   **tr**ain

Other Words

Write any words you and your teacher would like to add to this week's list.

—— —— —— ——

1. grass
2. bring
3. brave
4. drove
5. pretty
6. trap
7. brother
8. free
9. trunk
10. grew

grass
bring
brave
drove
pretty
trap
brother
free
trunk
grew

Pattern Power

Say each spelling word.

A. Write the words that begin with the letters below.

gr ___ ___   **dr** ___

tr ___ ___   **pr** ___

br ___   **fr** ___

___

___

B. What letter is the same in all the words? ___

Two consonant sounds blended together and spelled with two letters is called a **consonant cluster.**

54

Meaning Mastery

Write the spelling words that go with each group of words below.

1. lawn   mower   ___

2. elephant   tree   ___

3. brought   take   ___

4. hero   courage   ___

5. grow   grown   ___

6. drive   driven   ___

Dictionary Skills

Write each group of words in alphabetical order. You will need to look at the third letter in some words.

A. bring   1. ___   **B.** grass   1. ___

brave   2. ___   grew   2. ___

brother   3. ___   glad   3. ___

blind   4. ___   grow   4. ___

grass
bring
brave
drove
pretty
trap
brother
free
trunk
grew

Word Building

When a word ends in **s, sh, ch,** or **x,** add **-es** to make it plural. Add **-s** or **-es** to each word below to make it plural. Write the new word.

1. trunk _____

2. trap _____

3. box _____

4. grass _____

5. class _____

Writing Activities

Many words we use are **describing words.** They can tell much more about nouns. Read the sentences that follow. Which one tells you the most?

Please give me the ball.
Please give me the big red ball.

Add the describing word next to each sentence below to make a better sentence. Then write the new sentence.

1. Your sister looks just like you.   pretty

2. Those balloons are free.   yellow

Proofreading Practice

This sentence has mistakes in capitalization, spelling, and punctuation. Write the sentence correctly.

green gras grue in march

Review Words

Write the review words that begin with these letters.

from
trick
drop

1. **dr** ___   3. **fr** ___
2. **tr** ___

Challenge Words: Science

Use these science words to complete the story.

heat
hail
weather
warm
ice

   The (1)___ changes through the year. It is
(2)___ in the spring and fall. In the summer, there
is a lot of (3)___ . Sometimes it will (4)___ .
Some lakes are covered with (5)___ in the winter.

Review

Pattern Power

these
whole
thing
whistle

Lesson 7

Write the words that start with these letters.

1. **th** ___   ___
2. **wh** ___   ___

chair
shot
chew
shiny

Lesson 8

Write the words that start with these letters.

1. **ch** ___   ___
2. **sh** ___   ___

while
know
wheel
wrote

Lesson 9

Write the words that start with these letters.

1. **wh** ___   2. **kn** ___
   ___   3. **wr** ___

slip
blow
clean
glad

Lesson 10

Write the words that start with these letters.

1. **sl** ___   3. **bl** ___

2. **cl** ___   4. **gl** ___

Lesson 11

Write the words that start with these letters.

1. br ____   3. pr ____
2. tr ____   4. gr ____

Meaning Mastery

Use spelling words to complete these sentences about the story Alice in Wonderland. Use a word that begins with the letters shown under the blank.

1. Alice ____ tall when she ate a small cake.
   gr

2. The rabbit's watch was probably ____ .
   sh

3. They did not ____ the tea party dishes.
   cl

4. "And who are ____ ?" said the Queen, pointing to some cards.
   th

5. "How should I ____ ?" said Alice.
   kn

6. Alice had dreamed the ____ adventure.
   wh

these
whole
chair
shot
while
know
slip
blow
bring
pretty
thing
whistle
chew
shiny
wheel
wrote
clean
glad
trunk
grew

Word Building

A. Change the first two letters in each word below to make a word that tells about the picture. Write the word.

1.

slip ____

2.

grew ____

B. Add **-s** to each word below to make it plural.

1. whistle ____

2. wheel ____

3. chair ____

4. thing ____

5. trunk ____

C. Add **-es** to each word below to make it plural.

1. dress ____   4. bush ____

2. wish ____   5. fox ____

3. lunch ____

Dictionary Skills

Write each group of words in alphabetical order. You will need to look at the third letter in some words.

A. chew 1. ___   **B.** wrote 1. ___
    chair 2. ___   while 2. ___
    chill 3. ___   wheel 3. ___

Review Roundup

Can you find all the spelling words in this puzzle? Thirteen words go across. Seven words go up and down. One word has been done for you.

```
D A C E B F S H I N Y G J S
H K H I L N H M O P P T R U
Y X E W K N O W R O T E V P
Z A W H I S T L E C H A I R
C B H D G L A D E W H I L E
B L O W T H E S E H F H J T
O Q L K H B I C L E A N G T
T Y E Y I R W Z S E I P H Y
J E I G N I F T S L I P K N
U S M Q G N R T R U N K L O
A V M R B G R E W C R M A P
```

61

Spelling and Reading

these
whole
chair
shot
while
know
slip
blow
bring
pretty
thing
whistle
chew
shiny
wheel
wrote
clean
glad
trunk
grew

An author is someone who writes stories. Washington Irving is one of America's favorite authors. One of his best-known stories is "The Legend of Sleepy Hollow."
Read how Washington Irving tells about Ichabod Crane, a make-believe teacher.

Ichabod Crane was tall and thin. He had narrow shoulders and long arms and legs. His whole body was held loosely together. His hands hung a mile out of his sleeves. His head was small and flat. He had huge ears and green glassy eyes. He had a pointed nose. One might have thought he was a scarecrow in a cornfield.

Use the story to answer the questions below.

1. Which spelling word would you use to describe Ichabod Crane's eyes?
2. Did Ichabod Crane's hands really hang a mile out of his sleeves?
   How do you know?

The Writing Process

Prepare

Think about your favorite make-believe character. How would you describe this character to someone? Why do you like this character so much? Write your answers to these questions.

Write

Tell about your favorite character. Write down as many sentences as you can think of. Be sure to use describing words so your reader will know exactly what the character is like.

Revise

Read your sentences. Can you add any describing words to make your sentences tell better about what your character is like? Make sure your sentences are in the right order. Check each sentence. Does it begin with a capital letter? Does it end with a period? Are your words spelled correctly? Use editing marks to show where you want to make changes. Use your best handwriting to copy your sentences. Share your writing with a friend.

EDITING MARKS

indent or start a new paragraph	
use capital letter	
check spelling	
add letters or words	
take out	
add a period	

13 Consonant Clusters

1. store
2. step
3. swing
4. stand
5. spot
6. still
7. story
8. swim
9. state
10. stick

This Week's Words

Say each spelling word. Each word begins with two consonant sounds blended together. See how each word begins.

spill

stuck

sweep

Other Words

Write any words you and your teacher would like to add to this week's list.

— — — —

Pattern Power

Say each spelling word. Write the words that start with these letters.

st ___ ___ ___ ___

___ ___ ___

sw ___ ___

sp ___

Two consonant sounds blended together and spelled with two letters is called a **consonant cluster**.

store
step
swing
stand
spot
still
story
swim
state
stick

Meaning Mastery

Write the spelling word for each meaning.

1. a shop ___
2. to put one foot in front of the other ___
3. something to read or tell ___
4. a broken branch of a tree or bush ___

Dictionary Skills

There are two words at the top of each page in your **Spelling Dictionary/Thesaurus.** They are called **guide words.** The guide word on the left is the first word on that page. The guide word on the right is the last word on that page. Guide words help you find words in the dictionary.

Pretend the words in each box below are guide words on a dictionary page. Write the spelling words that would be found on a page with those guide words. The first one is done for you.

sport	stay

spot

___

___

storm	talk

___

___

Word Building

A. Add a letter to each word below to make a spelling word. The first one is done for you.

1. till _still_
2. wing ____
3. pot ____
4. tick ____

B. Add **st** to each word below to make a spelling word.

1. and ____
2. ate ____

Writing Activities

A **title** often comes before a person's name. Here are some titles that are often used.

Dr.   Ms.   Mr.   Miss   Mrs.

Notice that each title begins with a capital letter. Most of them end with a period. Also, remember that names begin with capital letters.

Write each of the names below correctly in a sentence. The first one is done for you.

1. dr gorman Dr. Gorman saw me.
2. miss gomez ____
3. ms ming ____
4. mr smith ____

Proofreading Practice

This sentence has mistakes in capitalization, punctuation, and spelling. Write the sentence correctly.

i saw my dentist, dr filmore, at the stor

Review Words

| sky |
| sled |
| stay |

Write the review words that begin with these letters.

1. **st** ___   3. **sl** ___

2. **sk** ___

Challenge Words: Math

| last |
| next |
| always |
| almost |
| mostly |

Match these words with the clues below.

1. at the end of the line   ___

2. every time   ___

3. for the greatest part   ___

4. the one that comes after this one ___

5. nearly   ___

Consonant Clusters

This Week's Words

Say each spelling word. Each word ends with two consonant sounds blended together. Notice how each word ends.

band   **sing**

thank   **tent**

Other Words

Write any words you and your teacher would like to add to this week's list.

___ ___ ___ ___

1. think
2. long
3. want
4. find
5. along
6. drink
7. bank
8. sent
9. ring
10. sing

think
long ✓
want
find
along ✓
drink
bank
sent
ring
sing

Pattern Power

Say each spelling word.

Write the words that end with the letters below.

ng ___   **nk** ___

___   ___

___   ___

___   **nt** ___

nd ___   ___

Two consonant sounds blended together and spelled with two letters is called a **consonant cluster.**

Meaning Mastery

Use spelling words to complete this story.

Many board games use play money. You keep the money in a

(1)____ . When you play a game, you have to (2)____ about what

you want to do. Sometimes you are (3)____ to a certain place on the

board. You might not (4)____ to be there. Some games take a

(5)____ time to play.

Dictionary Skills

Write these words in alphabetical order. Each group of words will
make a sentence. Start each sentence with a capital letter. End it
with a period.

1. ring find his can't bill

2. have trunks elephants long

think
long
want
find
along
drink
bank
sent
ring
sing

Word Building

Look at the two sentences below.

I sing well. He sings better

In the second sentence, **-s** was added to the word **sing.** Add **-s** to each word to make new words.

1. think ＿＿
2. ring ＿＿
3. drink ＿＿
4. want ＿＿
5. sing ＿＿
6. find ＿＿

Writing Activities

A **question** is a sentence that asks something. It starts with a capital letter and ends with a question mark, which looks like this ? .

Write these questions correctly.

1. who will sing that song

2. do you want to sing along

72

Proofreading Practice

A proofreader uses this editing mark ✗ to show that a letter or a word should be taken out of a sentence. This sentence has some mistakes. Make the changes shown by the editing marks. Write the sentence correctly.

<u>c</u>an ∧ **you** and <u>s</u>haron ⊙sig very well together ?∧

Review Words

Write the review words that end with these letters.

1. **nd** ____   3. **nk** ____
2. **nt** ____

went
friend
pink

Challenge Words: Social Studies

Use these words to complete the story.

England is part of Queen Elizabeth's (1)____ . Her son Charles is a (2)____ . Her daughter Ann is a (3)____ . The royal family lives in Buckingham (4)____ .

In olden days, kings and queens held dances where everyone wore a (5)____ .

kingdom
mask
palace
prince
princess

15 Words With ch and tch

1. such
2. each
3. catch
4. watch
5. beach
6. rich
7. bunch
8. match
9. touch
10. teach

This Week's Words

Say each spelling word. Each word ends with **ch** or **tch**. The sign for this ending is /ch/.

The word **lunch** ends with /ch/ spelled **ch**.

lun**ch**

The word **catch** ends with /ch/ spelled **tch**.

catch

Other Words

Write any words you and your teacher would like to add to this week's list.

—— —— —— ——

Pattern Power

Say each spelling word.

1. Write the words in which /ch/ is spelled **ch.**

—— —— —— —— —— —— ——

2. Write the words in which /ch/ is spelled **tch.**

—— —— ——

In most words, /ch/ is spelled **ch** or **tch.**

such
each
catch
watch
beach
rich
bunch
match
touch
teach

Meaning Mastery

Write a spelling word to answer each riddle.

1. What kind of sight tells time? ____

2. What has a head that can light a fire? ____

3. What can you do to a baseball and a fish? ____

Dictionary Skills

A dictionary tells what words mean and how they are used. The word you look up is the **entry word.** It is in dark print. An entry word and everything written about the word is called a **dictionary entry.** Look at each picture. Write the spelling word that would be the entry word for each one.

1.

2.

3.

Word Building

A. Add **-es** to each noun below to make it plural.

1. rich _____   3. match _____
2. beach _____   4. bunch _____

B. Add **-es** to each verb below.

1. touch _____   3. watch _____
2. teach _____   4. catch _____

C. Write the spelling words that rhyme with the word below.

much _____ _____

Writing Activities

PREPARE: Pretend you are going to the beach. Think of some food you can make for the trip.

WRITE: Write the directions to make that food. Write down everything you have to do.

REVISE: Read your sentences. Is there anything to add or take out? Make sure your directions are in order. Use editing marks to show your changes. Check for correct spelling. Copy your paper neatly.

Handwriting Practice

Practice your handwriting. Write this sentence.

Write each letter carefully.

Review Words

chop
children
duck

Write the review words that begin or end with the following letters.

1. ch _____ _____
2. ck _____

Challenge Words: Science

weed
butterfly
bud
reed
stem

Write the science words that match these meanings.

1. an unwanted plant _____

2. an adult caterpillar _____

3. a flower not yet opened _____

4. the part of the plant that holds the leaves _____

5. a tall, stemlike grass _____

Words With th and sh

This Week's Words

Say each spelling word. Each word ends with **th** or **sh.** The sign for the sound of **th** is /th/. The sign for the sound of **sh** is /sh/.

The word **fourth** ends with /th/ spelled **th.**

four**th**

The word **fish** ends with /sh/, spelled **sh.**

fi**sh**

1. wish
2. with
3. sixth
4. bush
5. bath
6. brush
7. wash
8. both
9. dish
10. teeth

Other Words

Write any words you and your teacher would like to add to this week's list.

___ ___ ___ ___

wish
with
sixth
bush
bath
brush
wash
both
dish
teeth

Pattern Power

Say each spelling word.

A. Write the words that end with /th/ spelled **th.**

___ ___ ___ ___ ___

B. Write the words that end with /sh/ spelled **sh.**

___ ___ ___ ___ ___

In most words, /th/ is spelled **th.** In most words, /sh/ is spelled **sh.**

Meaning Mastery

Good writers choose the best word for each sentence. Write the spelling word that could be used in place of the underlined word in each sentence.

1. I <u>clean</u> my dog at least two times a year. ___

2. He hates to take a <u>washing</u>. ___

3. We <u>together</u> get all wet. ___

4. He sometimes hides behind a <u>plant</u>. ___

Dictionary Skills

Each dictionary entry word is followed by a **definition**. A definition tells you what an entry word means. Write the spelling word that would be the entry word for each definition below.

1. ___ hard mouth parts used for chewing food

2. ___ something on which to place food

3. ___ the one after fifth

wish
with
sixth
bush
bath
brush
wash
both
dish
teeth

Word Building

The endings **-ed** and **-ing** can be added to many verbs.

start + ed = started   **start + ing = starting**

Add **-ed** and **-ing** to each verb below.

               -ed **-ing**

1. wish   ___ ___
2. brush ___ ___

Writing Activities

A letter has five parts: **heading, greeting, body, closing,** and **signature.** A comma is used in the heading date, the greeting, and the closing. Capital letters are used in the greeting, the closing, and for all proper names.

Heading → March 6, 1991
Greeting → Dear Lola,
Body →   Our new baby likes to splash in his bath. Mom let me brush his hair.
Closing → Your friend,
Signature → Ricardo

Write the part of the letter that has the words below.

1. Ricardo ___   3. Your friend, ___
2. Dear Lola, ___   4. March 6, 1991 ___

Proofreading Practice

The letter parts below have some mistakes in capitalization and punctuation.

Write them correctly.

1. with love   2. january 10 1991

Review Words

A. Write the review words that begin with these letters.

th ___ **sh** ___

B. Write the review word that ends with these letters.

sh ___

> **fish**
> **she**
> **the**

Challenge Words: Math

Write the math words that match these meanings.

1. before one and after another   ___

2. a group of things   ___

3. something to be worked out   ___

4. to put together   ___

5. two things that go together   ___

> **pair**
> **set**
> **between**
> **combine**
> **problem**

17

Words With Silent Letters

1. walk
2. light
3. could
4. climb
5. right
6. talk
7. sigh
8. would
9. lamb
10. caught

This Week's Words

Say each spelling word. Each word has one or two silent consonants.

The word **climb** ends with silent **b**.

clim**b**

The word **should** has a silent **l**.

shou**l**d

The word **talk** has a silent **l**.

ta**l**k

The word **high** has the silent letters **gh**.

hi**gh**

Other Words

Write any words you and your teacher would like to add to this week's list.

— — — —

Pattern Power

Say each spelling word.

A. Write the words that end in silent **b.**

___ ___

B. Write the words that have a silent **l.**

___ ___ ___ ___

C. Write the words that have the silent letters **gh.**

___ ___ ___ ___

In some words, the letters **b, l,** and **gh** may be silent.

walk

light

could

climb

right

talk

sigh

would

lamb

caught

Meaning Mastery

Use spelling words to complete these sentences.

1. Light, healthy foods are the ___ ones to choose.

2. It is better for your health to ___ steps than to ride the elevator.

3. When you are upset about something, you should ___ to someone about it.

4. To ___ outside every day is good exercise.

Dictionary Skills

A dictionary definition tells what an entry word means. Sometimes an **example sentence** follows a definition. This sentence uses the entry word to help you understand its meaning. Read the entry for **fire**.

> **fire** flame, heat, and light made by burning: *We cooked hot dogs over the fire.*

The example sentence is *We cooked hot dogs over the fire.*
Look up **lamb** in your **Spelling Dictionary/Thesaurus**. Write the example sentence.

Word Building

Write the spelling word that is a form of each word below. The first one is done for you.

1. walking <u>walk</u>
2. can ___
3. will ___
4. lit ___
5. catch ___

Writing Activities

Read this letter Cindy wrote to Jay.

June 11 1991

Dear Jay
   I have to help Dad on Friday night. Could we go to the show Saturday? Let me know soon.

        Your friend
        Cindy

Copy this letter. Add commas where they are needed.

Handwriting Practice

Practice your handwriting. Write this sentence.

The talking made me sigh.

Review Words

| eight |
| night |
| two |

Write the review words that have these silent letters.

1. gh ___ ___
2. w ___

Challenge Words: Social Studies

| grain |
| mill |
| nails |
| wire |
| build |

Use these social studies words to complete this paragraph.

To (1)___ a rabbit cage, you need wood, a hammer, and some (2)___ . Using a (3)___ fence for the sides gives the rabbit sunlight and air. You can go to a (4)___ to get (5)___ for your rabbit to eat.

Review

18

Pattern Power

Lesson 13
Write the words that begin with these letters.

1. sw ___   2. sp ___
    ___   3. st ___

| swing |
| spot |
| story |
| swim |

Lesson 14
Write the words that end with these letters.

1. nd ___   3. ng ___
2. nk ___   4. nt ___

| find |
| along |
| drink |
| sent |

Lesson 15
Write the words with /ch/ spelled these ways.

1. ch ___ ___
2. tch ___ ___

| each |
| catch |
| match |
| touch |

Lesson 16
Write the words that end with these letters.

1. th ___ ___
2. sh ___ ___

| wish |
| with |
| brush |
| both |

Lesson 17

Write the words that have these silent letters.

1. l ___   2. b ___
   ___   3. gh ___

Meaning Mastery

Write the spelling words to complete this paragraph. The answer begins or ends with the letters shown under each blank.

I walked in the woods (1)___ my friends. Our talking
                          th

(2)___ the birds flying. Mom said to be careful not to
  nt

(3)___ any plants we didn't know. We found a great
  ch

(4)___ for a picnic and decided we (5)___ come back soon.
  sp   **ld**

Word Building

Add **-s** or **-es** to each word below to make it plural.

A. 1. swing ____
2. brush ____
3. catch ____
4. match ____
5. wish ____

swing
spot
find
along
each
catch
wish
with
walk
right
story
swim
drink
sent
match
touch
brush
both
would
lamb

B. Add **-ed** and **-ing** to each verb below.

	-ed	-ing
1. walk	____	____
2. touch	____	____

C. Write the review word that is a form of each word below.

1. drank ____
2. send ____
3. found ____
4. swam ____

swing
spot
find
along
each
catch
wish
with
walk
right
story
swim
drink
sent
match
touch
brush
both
would
lamb

Dictionary Skills

nail   none

nest   a home made by a bird: *There is a bird's nest in our apple tree.*

Use the entry above to tell about the dictionary parts below.

1. entry word ____
2. definition ____
3. guide words ____ ____
4. example sentence ____

Review Roundup

Write a letter in each empty box to complete the spelling words. Boxes with matching numbers should have matching letters.

Grid 1:
¹	T	O	R	Y
¹	W	²	³	⁴
¹¹	L	⁵	³	⁴
B	R	⁶	¹	¹⁰
⁷	R	²	³	K
⁹	¹¹	¹²	⁹	¹⁰
¹²	⁵	⁶	⁹	¹⁰

Grid 2:
⁸	⁵	⁶	L	⁷
R	²	⁴	¹⁰	¹²
M	¹¹	¹²	⁹	¹⁰
F	²	³	⁷	
⁸	¹¹	L	K	
E	¹¹	⁹	¹⁰	
L	¹¹	M	B	

Grid 3:
⁸	²	¹	¹⁰
⁸	²	¹²	¹⁰
B	⁵	¹²	¹⁰
¹	W	²	M
¹	E	³	T
¹	P	⁵	T

92

Spelling and Reading

Read this letter. Find out what clothes a Florida cousin should bring when she comes north for a winter visit.

November 3, 1991

Dear Susan,

   I am so happy that you are coming to Minnesota to visit this winter. You will want to pack the right clothes. Bring a warm coat, a scarf, and some sweaters. Also, bring warm boots if you have them. I will be happy to share my warm clothes with you.

   We will walk in the snow along the lake. We will find lots of other fun things to do.

   I wish you were here with me right now.

Your cousin,
Amy

1. What does Amy think they will do in the snow?
2. Do you think Amy and Susan are about the same age?
   What makes you think so?

The Writing Process

Prepare

Think of what it takes to care for an animal. Perhaps you have a pet or you know someone who has one you like. Maybe you just know a lot about a certain kind of animal. Make notes about what you know about caring for this animal.

Write

Write a letter to a friend. Tell him or her how to care for your animal. Pretend your friend does not know anything about caring for your animal. You will need to tell about everything your friend needs to know.

Revise

Read your sentences. Does each one tell something important? Does each one tell something different? Does each sentence begin with a capital letter and end with a period? Are your words spelled right? Have you correctly written all the parts of a letter? If you made mistakes, use editing marks to change them. Copy your letter neatly. You may want to give or send it to a friend or your teacher.

EDITING MARKS

 indent or start a new paragraph

 use capital letter

 check spelling

 add letters or words

 take out

 add a period

Words With c, k, and ck

This Week's Words

Say each spelling word. Each word begins or ends with the sound of **k** as in **cat**. The sign for the **k** sound is /k/.

The word **cat** begins with /k/ spelled **c**.

cat

The word **kitten** begins with /k/ spelled **k**.

kitten

The word **black** ends with /k/ spelled **ck**.

bla**ck**

Other Words

Write any words you and your teacher would like to add to this week's list.

—— —— ——

1. kind
2. car
3. back
4. came
5. pick
6. coat
7. luck
8. wake
9. call
10. sick

kind

car

back

came

pick

coat

luck

wake

call

sick

Pattern Power

Say each spelling word.

A. Write the words that begin with /k/ spelled **c.**

—— —— —— ——

B. Write the words with /k/ spelled **k.**

—— ——

C. Write the words that end with /k/ spelled **ck.**

—— —— —— ——

In most words, /k/ is spelled **c, k,** or **ck.**

Meaning Mastery

Many words mean the opposite of another word. **Hot** and **cold** are opposites.

Write the spelling word that is the opposite of each word below.

1. mean ____
2. day ____
3. lost ____
4. well ____
5. front ____
6. went ____

Dictionary Skills

Some dictionary entries have more than one definition. Read each entry word and its meanings below. Write the entry word and the second definition for each word.

back **1** the rear part of the body: *Mitch has a fly on his back.* **2** the place at the rear: *Dan is in the back of the house.*

call **1** to speak in a loud voice: *Please call her to come home.* **2** to name: *I call my rabbit Pinky.* **3** to talk to by telephone: *I'll call you tonight.*

kind
car
back
came
pick
coat
luck
wake
call
sick

Word Building

To add **-ed** or **-ing** to a word that ends in **e**, you must drop the **e**. Look at the way you add **-ed** and **-ing** to the word **live**.

live + ed = lived   live + ing = living

Add **-ed** and **-ing** to each word below.

	-ed	-ing
1. wake	___	___
2. chase	___	___
3. change	___	___
4. whistle	___	___

Writing Activities

Copy the letter below. Add commas where they are needed.

March 10 1991

Dear Susan

   We were really in luck! We picked up our new car today. I helped put a coat of wax on it. We will come to see you next Saturday.

Your friend

Lynn

Handwriting Practice

Practice your handwriting. Write this sentence.

Did my call wake you up?

Review Words

Write the review words with /k/ spelled these ways.

1. **c** ____   3. **k** ____
2. **ck** ____

can
keep
black

Challenge Words: Science

Use these science words to match the clues below.

1. a large animal with antlers   ____
2. it looks like a butterfly   ____
3. a colorful talking bird   ____
4. it crawls along the ground   ____
5. it hops like a frog   ____

moth
moose
snake
toad
parrot

20

Double Letters

1. add
2. ball
3. fill
4. till
5. bell
6. fell
7. stuff
8. daddy
9. silly
10. egg

This Week's Words

Say each spelling word. Each word has a consonant sound spelled by the same two consonant letters. Notice the double consonants in each word.

ladd**er**   **o**ff

bigg**er**   **ye**ll**ow**

Other Words

Write any words you and your teacher would like to add to this week's list.

—— —— —— ——

Say each spelling word.

A. Write the words with **l** spelled **ll**.

—— —— —— —— —— ——

B. Write the word with **f** spelled **ff**.

——

C. Write the words with **d** spelled **dd**.

—— ——

D. Write the word with **g** spelled **gg**.

——

A consonant sound may be spelled with the same two consonant letters.

add
ball
fill
till
bell
fell
stuff
daddy
silly
egg

Meaning Mastery

Write the word in each group below that goes with the word in dark print.

1. **plus**   daddy   add   ___

2. **chicken**   bell   egg   ___

3. **father**   daddy   add   ___

4. **ring**   bell   ball   ___

5. **fall**   fell   fill   ___

Dictionary Skills

Pretend the words in each box below are guide words on a dictionary page. Write the spelling words that would be found on each page.

about   came

___

___

___

duck   flower

___

___

___

Word Building

Change the vowel in each word to the one next to the word. Write the new word.

1. well **i** ____

2. bell **a** ____

3. stiff **u** ____

4. fall **i** ____

5. tell **i** ____

Writing Activities

A sentence that shows excitement or surprise is called an **exclamation**. It ends with an **exclamation mark**. An exclamation mark looks like this. **!** Each sentence below ends with an exclamation mark.

What a great day!   **Wow!**

Write each sentence below as an exclamation. Put the right mark at the end of the sentence.

1. This is a swell bell.
2. This stuff is silly.

Proofreading Practice

The sentence below has some mistakes in spelling, capitalization, and punctuation. Write the sentence correctly.

1. where do the bel and bal belong

Review Words

off
will
yellow

Write the review words that have the following letters.

1. ll ____ ____

2. ff ____

Challenge Words: Math

empty
large
size
line
side

A. Write the math word that is the opposite of each word below.

1. small ____

2. full ____

B. Write the math words that match these clues.

1. straight mark ____

2. right or left part ____

3. how big or small ____

Double Letters

This Week's Words

Say each spelling word. Each word has a consonant sound spelled by the same two consonant letters. Notice the double consonants in each word.

penn**y** **pre**tt**y**

happ**y**

Other Words

Write any words you and your teacher would like to add to this week's list.

___ ___ ___ ___

1. little
2. penny
3. funny
4. apple
5. happy
6. kitten
7. better
8. cannot
9. dinner
10. puppy

little
penny
funny
apple
happy
kitten
better
cannot
dinner
puppy

Pattern Power

Say each spelling word.

A. Write the words with /n/ spelled **nn**.

— — — —

B. Write the words with /t/ spelled **tt**.

— — —

C. Write the words with /p/ spelled **pp**.

— — —

A consonant sound may be spelled with the same two consonant letters.

Meaning Mastery

Use spelling words to answer these riddles.

1. What girl's name is equal to one cent? _____

2. What can be red, yellow, or green and crunchy? _____

3. What kind of animal has a cat for a mother? _____

4. What else besides a tree has a bark? _____

Dictionary Skills

Write the spelling word that would be the entry word for each definition.

1. _____ the main meal of the day

2. _____ glad or pleased

3. _____ more good or more right

4. _____ small in size

little
penny
funny
apple
happy
kitten
better
cannot
dinner
puppy

Word Building

When a word ends in **consonant-y,** you must often change the **y** to **i** to add **-es.** Change the final **y** to **i** and add **-es** to the words below. The first one is done for you.

1. empty <u>empties</u>
2. penny ___
3. puppy ___
4. funny ___

Writing Activities

When you tell someone to do something, you are giving a command. Often you use a strong voice. These commands should have an exclamation mark after them. For example: **Watch out!** Write the sentences below. Add the exclamation mark.

1. Don't drop the apples

2. You cannot go

3. Don't burn your dinner

Handwriting Practice

Practice your handwriting. Write this sentence.

What a happy little kitten!

Review Words

Write the review words that have these double letters.

1. **ss** ___ ___
2. **ll** ___

dress
well
miss

Challenge Words: Social Studies

Write the social studies word that matches the clue.

1. smaller than a town ___
2. opening for a door ___
3. door for a fence ___
4. large town ___
5. a kind of home ___

gate
city
village
doorway
apartment

22

Words With /yü/ and /ü/

1. use
2. new
3. too
4. true
5. cool
6. cute
7. suit
8. room
9. do
10. move

This Week's Words

Say each spelling word. Each word has the vowel sound, as in **use** or **flew**. The signs for these sounds are /yü/ and /ü/. Notice how each sound is spelled.

/ü/	/yü/
balloon	**use**
flew	
fruit	

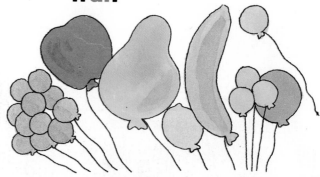

Other Words

Write any words you and your teacher would like to add to this week's list.

___ ___ ___

Pattern Power

Say each spelling word.

A. Write the words with /yü/ spelled **u-consonant-e.**

—— ——

B. Write the words with /ü/ spelled **oo.**

—— —— ——

C. Write the words with /ü/ spelled these ways.

ew ——   **ui** ——

D. Write the words with /ü/ spelled in other ways.

—— —— ——

In many words, /yü/ or /ü/ may be spelled **u-consonant-e, oo, ew,** or **ui.**

use
new
too
true
cool
cute
suit
room
do
move

Meaning Mastery

Use spelling words to complete the story below.

My new (1)___ is made of wool. It is nice to

wear when the weather is (2)___ . But I get

(3)___ warm in a hot (4)___ .

Dictionary Skills

Look up each word in your **Spelling Dictionary/Thesaurus.** Write
the example sentence.

1. new ___

2. cool ___

3. suit ___

4. cute ___

5. move ___

Word Building

A. Write the two words that rhyme in each set below.

    1. do, room, new ___ ___

    2. true, too, cute ___ ___

B. Change the first letter of **new** to the consonant clusters below. Write the new word.

    1. **bl** ___   3. **fl** ___

    2. **gr** ___   4. **dr** ___

Writing Activities

PREPARE: Is there a movie you would like to see? Pretend that your friend doesn't want to see the movie. Think of what you can say to talk your friend into going with you.

WRITE: Write some sentences to try to get your friend to go to the movie. Tell why you want to go to the movie. Why do you think your friend should go? What can you say to make him or her want to go? Try to use some spelling words.

REVISE: Read what you have written. Is there anything you want to add or take out? Check for spelling, capitalization, and punctuation. Use editing marks to show changes. Copy your sentences. Give them to your friend.

Proofreading Practice

The sentence below has some mistakes in spelling, capitalization and punctuation. Write the sentence correctly.

george asked if he could uz the fan

Review Words

blue
who
you

Write the review words with /yü/ or /ü/ with these letters.

1. **ue** ___   3. **o** ___
2. **ou** ___

Challenge Words: Science

cub
den
entry
sting
nest

Write the science words to complete the story below.

A young (1)___ went out of

its (2)___ . He went to a bee's

(3)___ in its hive. At the (4)___

he felt the first (5)___ . Away he

ran, zingity, zing.

Words With /ü/

This Week's Words

Say each spelling word. Each word has the vowel sound /ü/, as in **cook**. The word **cook** has /ü/ spelled **oo**.

cook

The word **bush** has /ü/ spelled **u**.

bush

The word **could** has /ü/ spelled **ou**.

could

Other Words

Write any words you and your teacher would like to add to this week's list.

—— —— —— ——

1. took
2. full
3. cook
4. put
5. should
6. foot
7. wood
8. look
9. book
10. pull

took
full
cook
put
should
foot
wood
look
book
pull

Pattern Power

Say each spelling word.

A. Write the words with /u̇/ spelled **oo.**

___ ___ ___ ___ ___ ___

B. Write the words with /u̇/ spelled **u.**

___ ___ ___

C. Write the word with /u̇/ spelled **ou.**

___

In many words, /u̇/ is spelled **oo, u,** or **ou.**

Meaning Mastery

Use spelling words to complete this paragraph.

Marta went to the library for a (1)___ . She found one about how to (2)___ foods. It was (3) ___ of pictures. She (4)___ it home to read. Then she (5)___ it to work to make a meal. But the meal was not good. She (6)___ have read the book more carefully.

Dictionary Skills

Read the definitions for the word **took**. Read the sentences below. Write the number of the definition that matches the meaning of the underlined word. The first one is done for you.

took 1 CARRIED **2** CHOSE **3** NEEDED

1. I <u>took</u> my lunch to school yesterday.   1

2. It <u>took</u> two people to move the chair. ___

3. I <u>took</u> the smallest cookie.   ___

took
full
cook
put
should
foot
wood
look
book
pull

Word Building

A. Write the spelling words that rhyme with each word below.

1. hook ___ ___ ___ ___
2. could ___ ___
3. bull ___ ___

B. To add **-ing** to a word that ends with a vowel and a consonant, you must double the consonant. Look at the way you add **-ing** to the word **get**. **get + t = getting.**

Add **-ing** to the words below.

1. put ___
2. slip ___
3. swim ___

Writing Activities

A **paragraph** is a group of sentences that tells about one main idea. The first word of a paragraph is **indented,** or moved in from the left. A paragraph usually begins with a main idea sentence. All of the other sentences in the paragraph should tell more about the main idea.

Use the main idea sentence below to write a paragraph.

There is one book I like more than any other.

Handwriting Practice

Practice your handwriting. Write this sentence.

The glass slipper fit her foot.

Review Words

Write the review words that have these letters.

1. **ee** ___ ___
2. **oo** ___

good
seed
need

Challenge Words: Math

Write the math words to match the numbers below.

1. 8th ___

2. 5th ___

3. 10th ___

4. 18 ___

5. 15 ___

eighteen
eighth
fifteen
fifth
tenth

Pattern Power

back
came
wake
sick

Lesson 19

Write the words with /k/ spelled these ways.

1. c ____   3. ck ____
2. k ____   ____

add
ball
daddy
egg

Lesson 20

Write the words that have these double consonants.

1. dd ____   2. ll ____
       ____   3. gg ____

little
penny
dinner
puppy

Lesson 21

Write the words that have these double consonants.

1. nn ____   2. tt ____
       ____   3. pp ____

use
too
suit
move

Lesson 22

Write the words with /yü/ or /ü/ spelled these ways.

1. u-consonant-e ____   3. ui ____
2. o-consonant-e ____   4. oo ____

Lesson 23

Write the words with /ù/ spelled these ways.

1. u ____   2. oo ____
   ____   3. ou ____

Meaning Mastery

A. Write the spelling word that is the opposite of each word below.

1. big   ____   4. well   ____
2. subtract   ____   5. went   ____
3. front   ____   6. sleep   ____

B. Use spelling words to complete this paragraph. Write a word that has the letter or letters shown after each blank.

Let's go to the pet store. We'll (1)____ (**u-consonant-e**) this

box to bring home a pet. I want the rabbit with a black spot on

its (2)____ (**ck**). We'll buy some greens for its (3)____ (**nn**).

121

back
came
add
ball
little
penny
use
too
put
should
wake
sick
daddy
egg
dinner
puppy
suit
move
look
pull

Word Building

A. Drop the last **e** and add **-ed** and **-ing** to these spelling words.

                  -ed   **-ing**

1. wake   ____   ____
2. move   ____   ____

B. Change the **y** to **i** and add **-es** to these spelling words.

1. penny ____   2. puppy ____

C. Double the final consonant and add **-ing** to these words.

1. put ____   2. cut ____

D. Change the vowel in **pat** to the letters **e, o,** and **u** to make new words.

____   ____   ____

Dictionary Skills

A. Pretend the words in each box are guide words on a dictionary page. Write the spelling words that would be found on each page.

pair	put

such	want

_____   _____
_____   _____
_____   _____
_____   _____

B. Find these words in your **Spelling Dictionary**. Write the first meaning.

1. puppy _____
2. add _____

Review Roundup

Unscramble these spelling words.

ddday _____   labl _____   seu _____
ienrnd _____   geg _____   tpu _____
sduolh _____   okol _____   mcea _____

123

Spelling and Reading

back
came
add
ball
little
penny
use
too
put
should
wake
sick
daddy
egg
dinner
puppy
suit
move
look
pull

A **fable** is a story that teaches a lesson. Read the fable to see how a little mouse could help a great lion.

A mouse ran over the nose of a sleeping lion. Surprised, the lion caught the mouse by the tail. He said, "I am going to eat you in one bite! You will be my dinner." "Please!" said the mouse. "Be kind and do not eat me. I am small but I will help you someday if you spare me."

The lion roared with laughter, but after thinking about what the mouse said, he let the mouse go.

Some time later the lion was caught in a rope trap. He could not get out.

Just then the mouse came by. The little mouse chewed on the ropes until they finally broke.

The lion learned that "No act of kindness, no matter how small, is ever wasted."

1. How did the mouse keep from getting eaten?

2. Why did the lion roar with laughter?

The Writing Process

Prepare

Think about a time when you helped someone do something. Was it something the person didn't think you could do? Did you have to talk the person into letting you help him or her? Who was the person? What did you say and do?

Write

Write as much as you can about the time you helped someone. Don't worry about making mistakes right now. You can fix them later.

Revise

Read what you have written. Is there anything else you can think of? Is there anything you want to take out? Are your sentences in the right order? Did you begin all proper nouns with capital letters? Check for correct punctuation. If you used sentences that were commands or showed strong feeling, did you end them with exclamation marks? Use editing marks to show where you want to make changes. Then copy your paragraph neatly. Share your paragraph with a friend.

EDITING MARKS

indent or start a new paragraph

use capital letter

check spelling

add letters or words

take out

add a period

25

Words With Long a

1. take
2. rain
3. cake
4. say
5. sale
6. baby
7. bake
8. same
9. today
10. great

This Week's Words

Say each spelling word. Each word has the long-**a** sound. The sign for the long-**a** sound is /ā/.
The long-**a** sound can be spelled **a**.

t**a**ble

The long-**a** sound can be spelled **a-consonant-e**.

wh**a**le

The long-**a** sound can be spelled **ai**.

t**ai**l

The long-**a** sound can be spelled **ay**.

gr**ay**

Other Words

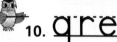

Write any words you and your teacher would like to add to this week's list.

— — —

Pattern Power

Say each spelling word.

A. Write the word with /ā/ spelled **a.**

B. Write the words with /ā/ spelled **a-consonant-e.**

----   ----   ----   ----   ----

C. Write the word with /ā/ spelled **ai.**

D. Write the words with /ā/ spelled **ay.**

----   ----

E. Write the word with /ā/ spelled another way.

In many words, /ā/ is spelled **a, a-consonant-e, ai,** or **ay.**

take
rain
cake
say
sale
baby
bake
same
today
great

Meaning Mastery

Write the spelling words that have the meanings below.

1. to cook food in an oven   ____
2. alike   ____
3. drops of water from the sky   ____
4. when prices are lowered   ____
5. to speak   ____
6. this day   ____

Dictionary Skills

A good writer uses the dictionary often. You know that many words have more than one meaning. A dictionary can help you find the right meaning. Write the underlined spelling word in each sentence. Find each word in your **Spelling Dictionary/Thesaurus.** Then write the number of the definition that tells how the word is used in the sentence. The first one is done for you.

1. We had a <u>great</u> time in school today.   _great_   2

2. Please get a new <u>cake</u> of soap from the cupboard.   ____ ____

3. Does it <u>take</u> you long to get to school?   ____ ____

128

Word Building

The ending **-er** can mean "more." For example, **smarter** means "more smart." Add **-er** to each word below. Change the final **y** to **i** before adding the ending to some words.

1. great ____
2. sick ____
3. new ____
4. happy ____
5. funny ____

take
rain
cake
say
sale
baby
bake
same
today
great

Writing Activities

Read each sentence.

Dorothy lived in Kansas.   **The lion** wanted to be brave.

The underlined part of each sentence tells what or whom the sentence is about. Write the part of each sentence below that tells what or whom the sentence is about.

1. The baby smiled at me. ____
2. The rain filled the tub. ____

Handwriting Practice

Practice your handwriting. Write this sentence.

What a great story!

Review Words

may
gave
train

Write the review words in which /ā/ is spelled these ways.

1. ai ___
2. a-consonant-e ___

3. ay ___

Challenge Words: Social Studies

gold
ocean
cliff
coal
lake

Write the social studies words that match these meanings.

1. a steep hill ___
2. rocks found under the ground ___

3. bodies of water ___

Words With Long e

This Week's Words

Say each spelling word. Each word has the long-**e** sound. The sign for the long-**e** sound is /ē/.

The long-**e** sound can be spelled these ways.

y or **ey**   **ea** or **ie**

only   **re**a**l**

monkey   **bel**ie**ve**

ee

see

Other Words

Write any words you and your teacher would like to add to this week's list.

___ ___ ___ ___

1. sea
2. many
3. meat
4. meet
5. money
6. seat
7. read
8. piece
9. only
10. people

sea
many
meat
meet
money
seat
read
piece
only
people

Pattern Power

Say each spelling word.

A. Write the words with /ē/ spelled **ea.**

____ ____ ____ ____

B. Write the word with /ē/ spelled **ee.**

____

C. Write the words with /ē/ spelled these ways.

y ____ ____

ey ____

D. Write the word with /ē/ spelled **ie.**

____

E. Write the word with /ē/ spelled a different way.

____

In many words, /ē/ is spelled
ea, ee, ie, y, or **ey.**

Meaning Mastery

sea
many
meat
meet
money
seat
read
piece
only
people

A. Write the spelling words that sound like the words below.

1. see ＿＿　　2. meet ＿＿

B. Use spelling words to complete these sentences.

1. Mary gave me milk ＿＿ Monday.
2. Mark made ＿＿ mistakes in math.
3. ＿＿ pay pennies to park.
4. Are you the ＿＿ one to win?

Dictionary Skills

A dictionary may have two entry words with the same spelling but different meanings. When this happens, numbers come before each word. Read the entries and the sentences after them. Write the number with the word that matches the meaning of the underlined word in each sentence. The first one is done for you.

1 ring a band to wear around a finger
2 ring to make a sound like the sound of a bell

1. Did you hear the telephone <u>ring</u>?　　<u>2</u>
2. Becky wears a gold <u>ring</u> on her finger.　＿＿

133

sea
many
meat
meet
money
seat
read
piece
only
people

Word Building

A. Add **-ing** to each word below.

1. meet ____   2. read ____

B. Add **-s** to each word below.

1. piece ____   2. seat ____

C. The ending **-er** can mean "one who does something." For example, one who pitches is a pitcher. Add **-er** to each word below. You may need to drop the last **e** before adding the ending.

1. read ____
2. use ____
3. bake ____
4. move ____

Writing Activities

PREPARE: Many stories are make-believe. Think of a make-believe place you would like to see. Make notes about what that place would be like. Use your spelling words for ideas.

WRITE: Write to tell about your make-believe place. Don't write a story. Just tell about your place.

REVISE: Read your sentences. Does each one tell something different about your make-believe place? Check your spelling and punctuation. Then write your sentences correctly on a clean piece of paper. Save your paper for another activity later.

Proofreading Practice

The proofreading mark that shows where a paragraph should start is:
¶ . The first word of a new paragraph should be moved in a little
way from the left. Make the changes shown by the editing marks
below. Write the paragraph correctly.

¶ there is a land far far away. the (peeple) live near a purple lake.

they use a large (peece) of shell for their (muny).

Review Words

Write the review words in which /ē/ is spelled
these ways.

1. ee ___   3. ea ___
2. e ___

be
see
please

Challenge Words: Science

Use these science words to complete the sentences
below.

1. A kitten has ___ fur.
2. ___ a cat's soft fur is nice.
3. The ___ of smell is not
   well understood.
4. ___ tells you that a
   lemon is sour.
5. Poison ivy can make you ___ .

feeling
itch
sense
soft
taste

Words With Long i

1. bike
2. dry
3. fine
4. tie
5. nice
6. mine
7. mind
8. buy
9. pie
10. fire

This Week's Words

Say each spelling word. Each word has the long-i sound. The sign for the long-i sound is /ī/.
The long-i sound can be spelled i.

find

The long-i sound can be spelled i-consonant-e.

nice

The long-i sound can be spelled y.

fly

The long-i sound can be spelled ie.

lie

Other Words

Write any words you and your teacher would like to add to this week's list.

___ ___ ___

Pattern Power

Say each spelling word.

A. Write the words with /ī/ spelled **i-consonant-e.**

   —— —— —— —— ——

B. Write the word with /ī/ spelled **y.**

   ——

C. Write the word with /ī/ spelled **i.**

   ——

D. Write the words with /ī/ spelled **ie.**

   —— ——

E. Write the word with /ī/ spelled another way.

   ——

In many words, /ī/ is spelled **i, i-consonant-e, y,** or **ie.**

bike
dry
fine
tie
nice
mine
mind
buy
pie
fire

Meaning Mastery

A. Write the word that is the opposite of each word below.

1. wet   ____
2. awful   ____
3. sell   ____
4. yours   ____
5. mean   ____

B. Write the spelling word to match each clue below.

1. a dessert   ____
2. flame, heat, and light   ____
3. to not like   ____
4. to make a knot   ____

Dictionary Skills

Read each entry below. Then read the sentences after the entry. Write the number of the definition that fits the meaning of each underlined word.

> **tie**   **1** a long piece of cloth worn around the neck   **2** the same in time or number

1. The game ended in a tie.   ____
2. Let's get Dad a new tie.   ____

Word Building

Add **-ing** to each word. You may need to drop the final **e** before adding **-ing**.

1. buy + ing ____

2. bike + ing ____

3. fire + ing ____

4. mine + ing ____

5. dry + ing ____

bike
dry
fine
tie
nice
mine
mind
buy
pie
fire

Writing Activities

Read each sentence.

Peter lived in the forest.   **He had an adventure in a garden.**

The underlined part of each sentence tells what is happening in the sentence. These parts tell what Peter Rabbit did. For each sentence below, write the part that tells what is happening in the sentence.

1. Renee rides a nice bike. ____
2. You made a fine pie. ____

Handwriting Practice

Practice your handwriting. Write this sentence.

Peter did not mind the rain.

Review Words

cry
hide
time

Write the review words in which /ī/ is spelled these ways.

1. **i-consonant-e** ___ ___
2. **y** ___

Challenge Words: Math

addition
plus
subtract
subtraction
sum

Use math words to complete this story.

   (1)___ and (2)___ are ways to work with numbers. When you add numbers, the answer is called a (3)___ . You take a small number away from a bigger number to (4)___ . A way of saying 2 + 2 is "two (5)___ two."

Words With Long o

This Week's Words

Say each spelling word. Each word has the long-**o** sound. The sign for the long-**o** sound is /ō/.

The long-**o** sound can be spelled these ways.

o

old

ow

snow

o-consonant-e

bone

oe

toe

oa

coat

1. boat
2. low
3. bone
4. goat
5. joke
6. load
7. grow
8. hope
9. soda
10. toe

Other Words

Write any words you and your teacher would like to add to this week's list.

___ ___ ___ ___

141

boat
low
bone
goat
joke
load
grow
hope
soda
toe

Pattern Power

Say each spelling word.

A. Write the word with /ō/ spelled **o**.

___

B. Write the words with /ō/ spelled **o-consonant-e.**

___ ___ ___

C. Write the words with /ō/ spelled **oa.**

___ ___ ___

D. Write the words with /ō/ spelled **ow.**

___ ___

E. Write the word with /ō/ spelled **oe.**

___

In many words, /ō/ is spelled **o, o-consonant-e, oa, ow,** or **oe.**

Meaning Mastery

Use spelling words to complete the rhyme below.

My brother told a funny ___ .
I laughed until my voice broke.
He said, "You should get something to drink.
This ___ will work, I think."
It did! I felt my voice ___ stronger.
But I was not laughing any longer.

boat
low
bone
goat
joke
load
grow
hope
soda
toe

Dictionary Skills

You can add **-ed, -es,** or **-ing** to most words without changing the spelling of the base word. If the spelling does change, a dictionary can help you spell the word correctly. Read this dictionary entry.

drop   dropped; dropping   to let fall: *Don't drop the dishes.*

Dropped and **dropping** are forms of the entry word **drop.**

Look up the entry words below in the **Spelling Dictionary/Thesaurus.** Write the other forms of the words.

1. joke   ___   ___   ___
2. hope   ___   ___   ___
3. grow   ___   ___   ___

boat
low
bone
goat
joke
load
grow
hope
soda
toe

Word Building

A. Write the spelling word that is the base word of each word.

1. joker   ____

2. boating   ____

3. grown   ____

4. lower   ____

B. Write the spelling words that rhyme with the words below.

1. cone ____   3. go ____

2. coat ____   ____

             ____   ____

Writing Activities

PREPARE: Think about the make-believe land you made up in Lesson 26. Think about the kinds of people and animals that are in your land.

WRITE: Make two lists. Call one list **People** and the other list **Animals.** Write down some thoughts you have about what the people and animals would be like in your make-believe land.

REVISE: Check your lists. Do you have anything to add or take out? Proofread your spelling. Use editing marks to make your changes. Copy your lists neatly. Save them for later.

Proofreading Practice

Read each sentence below. If there is a misspelled word, write it correctly.

1. A pioneer wagon carried a heavy lode. ____

2. The people were full of hoap. ____

Review Words

Write the review words in which /ō/ is spelled these ways.

open
hole
old

1. **o** ____ ____
2. **o-consonant-e** ____

Challenge Words: Social Studies

Use social studies words to finish these riddles. The last two words of the answer rhyme.

clothes
cap
mend
tore
hat

1. When you go to sleep, cover your head with a

   nap ____ .

2. Baseball players cover their heads with a

   bat ____ .

3. Socks could be called toes ____ .

4. If you ripped your shirt twice, you could say it was more ____ .

5. Mailing your ripped clothes to be fixed can be called a send ____ .

29

Words With /ȯ/

1. fall
2. water
3. also
4. onto
5. cost
6. because
7. saw
8. thought
9. log
10. gone

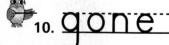

This Week's Words

Say each spelling word. Each word has the vowel sound, as in **frog**. The sign for this sound is /ȯ/.

The word **ball** has /ȯ/ spelled **a**.

ball

The word **frog** has /ȯ/ spelled **o**.

frog

The word **caught** has /ȯ/ spelled **au**.

caught

The word **paw** has /ȯ/ spelled **aw**.

paw

The word **bought** has /ȯ/ spelled **ou**.

bought

Other Words

Write any words you and your teacher would like to add to this week's list.

___ ___ ___ ___

Pattern Power

Say each spelling word.

A. Write the words with /ȯ/ spelled **a**.

___ ___ ___

B. Write the words with /ȯ/ spelled **o**.

___ ___ ___

C. Write the words with /ȯ/ spelled these ways.

au ___   **aw** ___

D. Write the word with /ȯ/ spelled **ou**.

___

E. Write the word with /ȯ/ spelled another way.

___

In many words, /ȯ/ is spelled **a, o, au, ou,** or **aw.**

fall
water
also
onto
cost
because
saw
thought
log
gone

Meaning Mastery

Use spelling words to complete this story.

How much does this turtle (1)____ ? I would like it (2)____ I'm making a model for school. I (3)____ need some rocks. Look! The turtle has (4)____ into its shell.

Dictionary Skills

Your **Spelling Dictionary/Thesaurus** also lists words that have the same or nearly the same meaning as an entry word. Read this entry.

boat   SHIP; something that sails on water

Look up the following words in your **Spelling Dictionary/Thesaurus**. Find the word below that means the same or nearly the same as each word.

saw	fall	thought	also

1. drop   ____
2. looked ____
3. too   ____
4. idea   ____

148

Word Building

Write the base word of each word below. You will need to add letters that were dropped when the ending was added. The first one is done for you.

1. riding   <u>ride</u>
2. living   __
3. sawing   __
4. falling   __
5. making   __
6. watering   __

fall
water
also
onto
cost
because
saw
thought
log
gone

Writing Activities

Write each sentence. Draw a circle around the words that tell what or whom the sentence is about. Draw a line under the words that tell what is happening in the sentence.

1. Nick saw me fall.

2. Todd fell off the log.

Proofreading Practice

A good proofreader makes a list of things to check for in writing. Write a checklist for the sentence below. Include spelling, capitalization, and punctuation. Check for one thing at a time. Then write the sentence.

red riding hood caught ontu the wolf's trick

Review Words

frog
dog
on

Write the review words that begin with these letters.

1. d ____   3. o ____
2. fr ____

Challenge Words: Science

safe
dark
wave
feel
hand

Use these science words to complete the story.

　　It was a (1)____ and stormy night. I could hear each (2)____ as it hit the beach. If I put my (3)____ out the window, I could (4)____ the cold rain. Thank goodness I was (5)____ and warm in my house.

Review

30

Pattern Power

Lesson 25

Write the long-**a** words that have these letters.

1. **ay** _____   3. **ai** _____
2. **a-consonant-e** _____   4. **ea** _____

take
rain
today
great

Lesson 26

Write the long-**e** words that have these letters.

1. **ee** _____   3. **ie** _____
2. **eo** _____   4. **ey** _____

meet
money
piece
people

Lesson 27

Write the long-**i** words that have these letters.

1. **i-consonant-e** _____   3. **ie** _____
2. **uy** _____   4. **y** _____

bike
dry
buy
pie

Lesson 28

Write the long-**o** words that have these letters.

1. **o-consonant-e** _____   3. **oa** _____
2. **ow** _____   4. **oe** _____

boat
joke
grow
toe

also
onto
because
thought

Lesson 29

Write the words in which /ȯ/ is spelled these ways.

1. o ___   3. au ___
2. a ___   4. ou ___

Meaning Mastery

A. Write the spelling word that means almost the same as these words.

1. now   present   ___
2. too   besides   ___
3. idea   thinking ___
4. cash   dollar   ___

B. Write the spelling word that means the opposite of each word below.

1. off ___   3. sell ___
2. give ___   4. wet ___

C. Use spelling words to complete this sentence.

Many (1)___ carry an umbrella in the (2)___ .

Word Building

take
rain
meet
money
bike
dry
boat
joke
also
onto
today
great
piece
people
buy
pie
grow
toe
because
thought

A. Add **-er** to each word below. Write the new word.

1. boat ____   3. great ____
2. bike ____   4. joke ____

B. Add **-ing** to each word below. Drop the final **e** for some words.

1. rain ____   4. buy ____
2. bike ____   5. joke ____
3. take ____   6. grow ____

C. Write the spelling words that rhyme with the words below.

1. date ____
2. seat ____
3. rake ____
4. coat ____
5. slow ____ ____
6. sky ____ ____ ____

153

take
rain
today
great
meet
money
piece
people
bike
dry
buy
pie
boat
joke
grow
toe
also
onto
because
thought

Dictionary Skills

A. Read the definition for the word **great**. Then read the sentence. Write the number of the definition that matches the meaning of the underlined word.

great **1** very important **2** very good

1. The circus was <u>great</u>! ____

B. Look up the words below in your **Spelling Dictionary/Thesaurus**. Write the other forms of the entry words.

1. meet ____ ____
2. buy ____ ____

Review Roundup

Can you find all the spelling words in this puzzle? Eleven words go across. Nine words go up and down. Circle each word as you find it.

```
T H O U G H T D E R Q B
O P I E R A I N B M A E
D R Y G E P I E C E F C
A L S O A E H B I E J A
Y B U Y T O T O N T O U
O I N M L P O A K J K S
P K R S U L E T A K E E
B E M O N E Y T G R O W
```

Spelling and Reading

Dorothy and her dog Toto traveled to the imaginary land of Oz in the book, The Wizard of Oz. Read to find out whom she met there.

On her way to meet the Wizard of Oz, Dorothy and her dog Toto came to a fork in the road.

All of a sudden, she heard a voice. "Some people like to go this way," the voice said.

"Who said that?" Dorothy asked. No one was there.

Toto ran over and started barking at a funny, dry scarecrow standing in a field. The scarecrow crossed its arms and said, "People go both ways!"

Dorothy thought it must be some kind of a joke because she knew that scarecrows couldn't talk.

"I don't know which way, because I don't have a brain," the scarecrow said. "I'm pleased to meet you."

Dorothy said she was pleased to meet him, too. She helped him down from his post. Dorothy said she wouldn't mind if they traveled together to meet the great wizard. Maybe he would help both of them.

1. Who goes one way or another on the road?

   ——

2. What words describe the scarecrow?

   —— ——

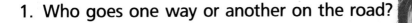

The Writing Process

Prepare

You have been thinking about an imaginary land in this unit. So far, you have thought about what the land looks like and what kind of people and animals are in it. Now you can make up a story about your land and people. A good story has something interesting or exciting happen in it.

Write

Write down some sentences that tell a story about your land and people. Use the lists you have saved about the land and its people. Don't worry about making mistakes. You can fix them later.

EDITING MARKS

 indent or start a new paragraph

 use capital letter

 check spelling

 add letters or words

 take out

 add a period

Revise

Read your sentences. Are they in the right order? Make sure you need each sentence. Use editing marks to make changes. Proofread for mistakes in spelling, capitalization, and punctuation. Now copy your story neatly and make it into a book for other people to read.

Words With ou and ow

This Week's Words

Say each spelling word. Each word has the vowel sound, as in **found**. The sign for this sound is /ou/.

The word **found** has /ou/ spelled **ou**.

fo**und**

The word **brown** has /ou/ spelled **ow**.

b**row**n

Other Words

Write any words you and your teacher would like to add to this week's list.

—— —— —— ——

1. house
2. how
3. our
4. bow
5. flower
6. about
7. now
8. cow
9. sound
10. town

157

house
how
our
bow
flower
about
now
cow
sound
town

Pattern Power

Say each spelling word.

A. Write the words with /ou/ spelled **ou**.

—— ——

—— ——

B. Write the words with /ou/ spelled **ow**.

—— —— ——

—— —— ——

In most words, /ou/ is spelled **ou** or **ow**.

Meaning Mastery

Write the spelling word that has almost the same meaning as each numbered word below.

1. noise ____   3. city ____

2. home ____   4. almost ____

*house
how
our
bow
flower
about
now
cow
sound
town*

Dictionary Skills

Pretend the words in each box below are guide words on a dictionary page. Write the spelling words that would be found on a dictionary page with those guide words. The first one is done for you.

floor	hundred

flower
____
____

about	cry

____
____
____

house
how
our
bow
flower
about
now
cow
sound
town

Word Building

Add **-s** to each word below to make it plural.

1. house _____   4. cow _____
2. bow _____   5. sound _____
3. flower _____   6. town _____

Writing Activities

The parts of this letter are not in order. Write the letter, and put each part where it should be.

Love,   Dear Marcos,
    Our house is near a small
town. Now we hear different
sounds. Come down soon.
April 9, 1991   Betty

Handwriting Practice

Practice your handwriting. Write this sentence.

Flowers grow well at our house.

Review Words

Write the review words that have /ou/ spelled these ways.

brown
down
found

1. ow ___ ___
2. ou ___

Challenge Words: Math

Write the math word that matches each clue below.

paid
cent
none
wages
bill

1. money earned ___
2. money spent ___
3. penny ___
4. paper money ___
5. zero ___

32

1. hard
2. start
3. arm
4. far
5. part
6. party
7. yard
8. are
9. farm
10. barn

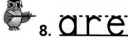

Words With /är/

This Week's Words

Say each spelling word. Each word has the vowel sound, as in **car**. The sign for this sound is /är/.

This /är/ sound is usually spelled **ar**.

car   **garden**

Other Words

Write any words you and your teacher would like to add to this week's list.

___ ___ ___ ___

Pattern Power

Say each spelling word.

Write the words that rhyme with these words.

1. card   ___ ___
2. jar   ___ ___
3. cart   ___ ___
4. harm   ___ ___
5. yarn   ___
6. hearty   ___

In most words, /är/ is spelled **ar**.

hard
start
arm
far
part
party
yard
are
farm
barn

Meaning Mastery

A. Write the spelling word that means the opposite of each word below.

1. stop ___   2. whole ___

B. Use spelling words to complete this poem.

Let's have a (1)___ . Just you and me.

It isn't my birthday, so don't buy a card.

We'll play in the house and the (2)___ .

We'll have fun wherever we (3)___ .

We won't give a darn, we'll play in the (4)___ .

Dictionary Skills

Look up these words in the **Spelling Dictionary/Thesaurus.** Write the forms of the word.

1. write ___ ___ ___
2. start ___ ___
3. far ___ ___
4. hard ___ ___

Word Building

A. Add **-ing** to each word below. Double the final consonant before adding the ending.

1. clap   ——
2. drop   ——
3. skip   ——
4. run   ——

B. Add **-es** to the spelling word below to make it plural. Change the **y** to **i**.

party   ——

hard
start
arm
far
part
party
yard
are
farm
barn

Writing Activities

PREPARE: Think about some time when you were really happy. Remember everything that happened.

WRITE: Write these words across the top of a piece of paper: **see, hear, feel, smell, taste.** Now write words in each list that tell what you saw, heard, felt, smelled, and tasted.

REVISE: Read each list. Be sure you have each word in the right list. Are there words you can add? Proofread for spelling mistakes. Use editing marks to make any changes. Copy your lists neatly. Save your work for later.

Proofreading Practice

Proofread the sentence below for misspelled words. Write the sentence correctly.

Bart broke his arme on the farme.

Review Words

Write the review words that have these letters.

1. ee _____   3. o_____
2. a-consonant-e _____

Challenge Words: Social Studies

Use these social studies words to complete this paragraph.

   Carla rode on a wooden (1)_____ to visit a farm. She saw a bale of (2)_____ for the cows to eat. Carla held a tiny (3)_____ in her hands. She also fed fresh (4)_____ to a baby calf. The farmer even let her feed corn to his (5)_____ named Oink.

Words With /ər/

This Week's Words

Say each spelling word. Each word ends with the vowel sound, as in **faster**. The sign for this sound is /ər/.

The word **faster** ends with /ər/ spelled **er**.

fast**er**

The word **tractor** ends with /ər/ spelled **or**.

tract**or**

Other Words

Write any words you and your teacher would like to add to this week's list.

___ ___ ___ ___

1. color
2. other
3. never
4. number
5. winter
6. father
7. mother
8. teacher
9. sister
10. doctor

color
other
never
number
winter
father
mother
teacher
sister
doctor

Pattern Power

Say each spelling word.

A. Write the words in which /ər/ is spelled **er.**

—— —— —— —— —— ——

—— ——

B. Write the words in which /ər/ is spelled **or.**

—— ——

In most words, /ər/ is spelled **er** or **or.**

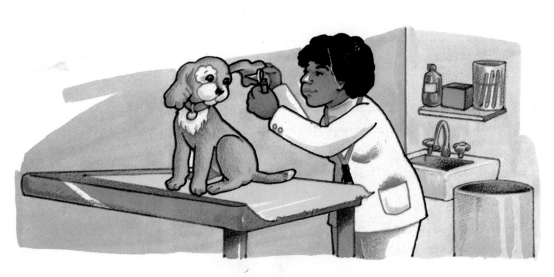

Meaning Mastery

A. Write the spelling words that name members of a family.

___ ___ ___

B. Write the spelling word that goes with each group of words below.

1. dentist, nurse, hospital ___

2. school, class, principal ___

3. ever, always, sometimes ___

color
other
never
number
winter
father
mother
teacher
sister
doctor

Dictionary Skills

Read the entry below.

> **winter**   the time of the year between fall and spring: *Where I live, it snows in winter.*

1. Write the entry word. ___
2. Write the definition. ___
3. Write the example sentence. ___

Word Building

color
other
never
number
winter
father
mother
teacher
sister
doctor

A. Add **-s** and **-ing** to each word below. Drop the final **e** before adding the **-ing** ending.

		-es	-ing
1.	come	___	___
2.	write	___	___
3.	use	___	___
4.	chase	___	___
5.	number	___	___

B. Write the two spelling words that rhyme.

___ ___

Writing Activities

PREPARE: Get the lists you wrote in Lesson 32. Look at your words. Think about how you felt during that happy time.

WRITE: Write some sentences to tell about the happy time you are writing about. You might want to use rhyming words. Can you put the words together to make a poem?

REVISE: Read what you have written. Change your words around until you get the sound you want. You may have to try more than once. Then copy your poem neatly. Share it with a friend.

170

Proofreading Practice

This question contains mistakes in spelling, capitalization, and punctuation. Write the sentence correctly.

what culer is the sky in july

Review Words

Write the review words that have these letters.

1. **ear** ____
2. **er** ____ ____

after
bear
over

Challenge Words: Science

Write the science word to match the clue.

1. a bird like a duck ____
2. to look quickly ____
3. the sound a young bird makes ____
4. to look for ____
5. something used to catch fish ____

bait
hunt
peek
peep
goose

34 Words With /or/

1. before
2. horse
3. more
4. for

5. door
6. born
7. morning
8. corn
9. forgot
10. shore

This Week's Words

Say each spelling word. Each word has the vowel sound, as in **horn**. The sign for this sound is /or/. The word **horn** has /or/ spelled **or**.

horn

The word **store** has /or/ spelled **ore**.

store

Other Words

Write any words you and your teacher would like to add to this week's list.

___ ___ ___ ___

Pattern Power

Say each spelling word.

A. Write the words in which /ȯr/ is spelled **or**.

—— —— ——
—— —— ——

B. Write the words in which /ȯr/ is spelled **ore**.

—— —— ——

C. Write the word in which /ȯr/ is spelled a different way.

——

In most words, /ȯr/ is spelled **or** or **ore**.

before
horse
more
for
door
born
morning
corn
forgot
shore

Meaning Mastery

Use spelling words to complete the paragraph below.

On our farm, we get up (1)____ it is light. We get a lot of work done in the (2)____ while it is still cool. This year, we grew (3)____ ears of (4)____ than we did last year.

Dictionary Skills

Write a spelling word that means the same or nearly the same as each word below.

1. ahead ____   4. birth ____
2. coast ____   5. gate ____
3. added ____   6. dawn ____

Word Building

Write the word that is a form of each word below.

1. horses   ____
2. doors   ____
3. shores   ____
4. forgotten   ____

before
horse
more
for
door
born
morning
corn
forgot
shore

Writing Activities

Write each sentence below. Draw a circle around the words that tell what the sentence is about. Draw a line under the words that tell what is happening in the sentence.

1. Darla brushed the horse.

2. Tom closed the door.

3. The goose swam for the shore.

175

Handwriting Practice

Practice your handwriting. Write this sentence.

The horse was born in the morning.

Review Words

Write the review words that have these letters.

1. **oor** _____   3. **our** _____
2. **or** _____

Challenge Words: Math

A. Write the math words that are used to measure distance.

_____ _____

B. Write the math words that are used to measure weight.

_____ _____

C. Write the math word that is used to measure liquid.

_____

Words With /ur/

This Week's Words

Say each spelling word. Each word has the vowel sound, as in **her**. The sign for this sound is **/ur/**.

The word **third** has /ur/ spelled **ir**.

third

The word **world** has /ur/ spelled **or**.

world

The word **turtle** has /ur/ spelled **ur**.

turtle

The word **learn** has /ur/ spelled **ear**.

learn

Other Words

Write any words you and your teacher would like to add to this week's list.

___ ___ ___ ___

1. first
2. were
3. girl
4. work
5. hurt
6. turn
7. fur
8. shirt
9. birthday
10. heard

first
were
girl
work
hurt
turn
fur
shirt
birthday
heard

Pattern Power

Say each spelling word.

A. Write the word in which /ur/ is spelled **ere**.

———

B. Write the words in which /ur/ is spelled **ir**.

—— —— —— ——

C. Write the word in which /ur/ is spelled **or**.

———

D. Write the words in which /ur/ is spelled **ur**.

—— —— ——

E. Write the word in which /ur/ is spelled **ear**.

———

In many words, /ur/ is spelled **ir, or, ur,** or **ear.**

Meaning Mastery

Use spelling words to finish these riddles.
The last two words in the answer rhyme.

1. A piece of clothing you drop in the mud is a dirt ___ .
2. A cat's hair is purr ___ .
3. A balloon that pops before any other is the ___ burst.

first
were
girl
work
hurt
turn
fur
shirt
birthday
heard

Dictionary Skills

Read the entries and the sentences after them. Write the number with the word that matches the meaning of the underlined word in each sentence. The first one is done for you.

¹**work**   a job
²**work**   to do a job

1. They <u>work</u> in the fields.   <u>2 work</u>
2. Farming is hard <u>work</u>.   ___

¹**rock**   a large stone
²**rock**   to move back and forth or from side to side

3. I can <u>rock</u> in this old chair.   ___

179

first
were
girl
work
hurt
turn
fur
shirt
birthday
heard

Word Building

Write the spelling words that rhyme with these words.

1. her   ___   ___
2. curl   ___
3. bird   ___

Writing Activities

You have learned about four different kinds of sentences this year. One kind of sentence tells something. It ends in a period. Another kind asks something. It ends in a question mark. A third kind of sentence shows surprise. It ends in an exclamation mark. The fourth kind of sentence also ends in an exclamation mark. This kind of sentence gives a strong command. Using the words **happy birthday,** write an example of each kind of sentence.

1. ___   3. ___
2. ___   4. ___

Proofreading Practice

Proofread each sentence below for misspelled words. Write each word correctly.

1. It is my tern to read. ____
2. Both girls were in ferst grade. ____
3. It is Dad's turn to take care of the hirt bird. ____

Review Words

Write the review words that have these sounds.

1. /ur/ ____ ____
2. /a/ ____

her
bat
bird

Challenge Words: Social Studies

Use the social studies words to complete the sentences below.

1. My three favorite ball games are ____ , ____ , and ____ .
2. I like rock and roll ____ the best.
3. Our band will march in a ____ tomorrow.

music
parade
softball
basketball
baseball

181

Review

Pattern Power

how **our** **about** **town**	### Lesson 31 Write the words with /ou/ spelled these ways. 1. **ou** ___ ___ 2. **ow** ___ ___
start **far** **party** **are**	### Lesson 32 Write the words that rhyme with the words below. 1. car ___ 2. part ___ ___ 3. hearty ___
color **number** **mother** **doctor**	### Lesson 33 Write the words that end with these letters. 1. **er** ___ ___ 2. **or** ___ ___
before **door** **morning** **corn**	### Lesson 34 Write the words that have these letters. 1. **or** ___ 2. **oor** ___ ___ 3. **ore** ___

Lesson 35

Write the words in which /ur/ is spelled these ways.

1. **ir** ___   3. **or** ___
2. **ur** ___   4. **ear** ___

Meaning Mastery

A. Use spelling words to complete this paragraph.

    I was not feeling well, so I went to see the (1)___ . He asked me (2) ___ I was feeling. I told him (3)___ my sore throat. He said he (4)___ a little something in my chest. "Here (5)___ some notes on things to do," he said. I really like (6)___ doctor.

B. Write the spelling word that means the opposite of each word below.

    1. stop ___   2. near ___

C. Write the spelling word that means almost the same as each word below.

    1. city ___   2. begin ___

how
our
start
far
color
number
before
door
first
work
about
town
party
are
mother
doctor
morning
corn
fur
heard

Word Building

A. Add **-s** to each word below to make it plural. Write the new word.

1. door ____   3. color ____
2. town ____   4. number ____

B. Change the **y** to **i** and add **-es** to these words to make them plural.

1. party ____   2. puppy ____

C. Add **-ed** and **-ing** to these words. Double the final consonant before adding the endings.

        -ed -ing

1. stop ____ ____
2. slip ____ ____

D. Add **-ing** to these words. In some words, drop the final **e** before adding the ending.

1. serve ____
2. work ____

Dictionary Skills

Pretend the words in each box below are guide words on a dictionary page. Write the spelling words from this lesson that would be found on each page.

also	could

—
—
—
—

many	pair

—
—
—
—

Review Roundup

Unscramble these words.

efbeor ___

hmtoer ___

oorcl ___

ordtco ___

ttars ___

ristf ___

earhd ___

munreb ___

rfu ___

korw ___

odro ___

cnor ___

how
our
start
far
color
number
before
door
first
work
about
town
party
are
mother
doctor
morning
corn
fur
heard

Spelling and Reading

Many poems are written about the weather. Read how Robert Louis Stevenson wrote about the wind.

I saw you toss the kites on high
And blow the birds about the sky;
And all around I heard you pass,
Like ladies' skirts across the grass—
   O wind, a-blowing all day long,
   O wind, that sings so loud a song!

I saw the different things you did,
But always you yourself you hid.
I felt you push, I heard you call,
I could not see yourself at all—
   O wind, a-blowing all day long,
   O wind, that sings so loud a song!

1. Write three rhyming-word pairs from the poem.
2. Write the first line from the poem that tells how he knew the wind was there.

The Writing Process

Prepare

Do you have a favorite time of year? Decide what time of year you would like to write a poem about.

Write

Make notes about what you like best about that time of year. List what you see, hear, taste, and feel during your favorite season. Write down as many thoughts as you can. Don't worry about making mistakes. You can make changes later.

Revise

Read what you have written. Think about how you put your ideas together. Are there any words you want to rhyme? Try moving some of your words around until you get the sounds you want. Proofread for spelling mistakes. Use editing marks to show your changes. Then copy your poem neatly. Perhaps your class can make a book of poems.

EDITING MARKS

indent or start a new paragraph	
use capital letter	
check spelling	
add letters or words	
take out	
add a period	

STUDENT SPELLING HANDBOOK

CONTENTS

Helpful Hints for Spelling

These steps may help if you have trouble spelling a word.

1. Think of a word you know that has the same spelling pattern, like a rhyming word. (**say, hay, day**)

2. Change the way you say the word to make it sound longer. (**bas ket ball**)

3. Keep a notebook with a list of the words you have trouble spelling. Put the words in alphabetical order so you can find them easily.

4. Make up clues to help you remember the spelling. (**chair = ch on air**)

5. Write the word in different ways to see which one looks correct. (**ceet, seet, seat**)

6. Find a smaller word in the word. (**You heard with your ear.**)

7. Break the word into word parts or syllables. (**but ter fly**)

8. Think of a word that has the same base word. (**take- tak ing**)

9. Learn the basic spelling rules found on page **190** of this handbook.

10. Use the Word Study Steps found on page **iii** to help you learn the spelling.

11. Become familiar with the dictionary and use it often.

Basic Spelling Rules

Learning these rules can help you spell many words.

1. When words end in silent **e,** drop the **e** when adding an ending that begins with a vowel. (**move + ed = moved**)

2. When a base word ends with **y,** change the **y** to **i** when adding the ending. (**party + es = parties**)

3. When a base word ends with a vowel followed by **y,** do not change the ending when adding endings. (**monkey = monkeys**)

4. When a one-syllable word ends in one vowel followed by one consonant, double the consonant before adding an ending that begins with a vowel. (**swim + ing = swimming; drop + ed = dropped**)

5. The letter **q** is always followed by **u.** (**quart**)

6. No English words end in **v.**

7. Add **-s** to most words to form plurals. Add **-es** to words ending in **x, z, s, sh,** or **ch.** (**car = cars; box = boxes**)

8. When choosing **ei** or **ie,** remember that **i** comes before **e** except after **c** or when sounded like /ā/ as in **neighbor** or **weigh.**

Common Spelling Patterns

Below is a list of sounds and different ways sounds are spelled. Use this list when you can't find a word in the dictionary, to see how else the sound may be spelled.

/a/	a	apple, bat	/ō/	o	go, so
/ā/	a-e	take, ate		o-e	home, nose
	a	table, baby		oa	boat, load
	ai	rain, nail		ow	low, slow
	ay	say, day	/ȯ/	a	ball, water
/är/	ar	hard, yard		o	on, dog
/ch/	ch	lunch, chair		au	caught, because
	tch	catch, match		aw	paw, saw
/d/	d	bed, add	/ȯr/	or	for, born
	ld	could, would		ore	before, more
/e/	e	bed, over	/ou/	ou	house, about
/ē/	e	we, me		ow	how, down
	ea	real, eat	/r/	r	red, rain
	ee	tree, meet		wr	wrote, wrong
	y	only, many	/sh/	sh	shop, fish
	ey	monkey, money	/Ŧh/	th	that, these
/hw/	wh	where, whistle	/th/	th	thank, fourth
/i/	i	if, bit	/u/	u	cut, must
/ī/	i	ice, mind	/u̇/	u	full, put
	i-e	like, time		oo	foot, look
	y	buy, my	/ü/	oo	moose, too
/k/	c	cat, car		ew	flew, new
	k	kitten, kind		ui	suit, fruit
	ck	pick, black	/ur/	er	her, serve
	lk	walk, talk		ir	girl, bird
/m/	m	from, them		or	world, work
	mb	climb, lamb		ur	hurt, fur
/n/	n	nice, not	/yü/	u-e	use, cute
	kn	know, knew	/ər/	ar	dollar, collar
/o/	o	hot, top		er	other, never
				or	color, doctor

Words You Often Use

Here is a list of words that are among the most common words used in writing. Use this list to check your spelling or knowledge of these words.

able	brother	from	money	school	under
about	by	fun	more	see	until
above	call	going	mother	she	up
after	came	good	much	sister	us
again	children	got	my	so	use
against	clean	green	name	some	very
all	come	had	never	started	want
almost	could	have	night	take	was
also	day	help	not	tell	water
always	didn't	her	now	that	we
another	do	him	of	the	well
any	does	his	once	their	went
are	don't	home	one	them	were
around	down	house	or	then	what
as	easy	how	other	there	when
asked	eat	I	our	they	where
away	even	into	out	thing	will
back	every	is	own	this	with
because	family	just	people	thought	work
been	father	know	play	through	would
before	first	like	put	time	yellow
best	food	little	red	to	you
better	for	look	right	too	your
between	found	make	said	try	
blue	friend	many	saw	two	

Difficult Words to Spell

These words often cause spelling problems for writers. Use this list to check your spelling or to test yourself to see how many of these words you can spell correctly.

again	decide	January	quite
all right	dictionary	library	really
always	enough	listen	rhyme
answer	every	lose	school
awful	favorite	minute	stretch
because	February	neighbor	surprise
bicycle	finally	nickel	they're
built	forty	ninth	though
caught	fourth	often	through
children	friend	people	two
clothes	guess	probably	we'll
cough	half	quiet	we're
cousin	hour	quit	were

Common Homophones

Homophones are words that sound the same but have different spellings and meanings. Use this list of homophones to help you decide which word to use.

ant	blew	eye	hour	meat	some	wood
aunt	blue	I	our	meet	sum	would
bare	buy	flour	knew	read	their	to
bear	by	flower	new	reed	there	too
						two
be	dear	hear	know	sea	threw	
bee	deer	here	no	see	through	

A Writing Plan

Writing is a way to share facts, ideas, or feelings. Writing can be easy if you take it one step at a time. The following steps can help you become a good writer.

PREPARE

This step will help you put your thoughts in order. In this step, answer these questions.

1. Who will be your readers (audience)?
2. What is your purpose for writing?
   - to express your feelings
   - to describe
   - to give information
   - to persuade
   - to tell a story
   - to write a poem
3. Do you need to find out more about your chosen topic? How can you learn more about the topic?
   - read
   - talk to other people
   - watch a movie
4. How will you remember what you want to include in your writing?
   - take notes
   - make a list

WRITE

As soon as possible after you have gathered your information, write it in sentence form for ten minutes without stopping. Don't worry about your spelling or whether your words will make sense to anyone else. Just let your thoughts flow. Get all of your thoughts down.

REVISE

Read over your writing and answer these questions.

1. Did you write to your audience?
2. Did you achieve your purpose for writing?
3. Did you include everything you wanted to? Did you say too much?
4. Are there any sentences or thoughts that do not fit in or should be moved?
5. Does each sentence express a complete thought?
6. Does your writing have a beginning, middle, and end?
7. Proofread your work. Use the proofreading checklist below.

Proofreading Checklist

- Are all words spelled correctly?
- Does each sentence begin with a capital letter?
- Does each sentence end with the correct punctuation?
- Are all paragraphs indented?
- Are all proper nouns capitalized?
- Did you use all words correctly?
- Have you dotted all **i's** and **j's** carefully? Have you crossed all **t's, f's,** and **x's?**
- Is your handwriting clear and easy to read?
- Have you cleanly erased or clearly crossed out any material you do not want?

8. Make a clean, neat copy of your writing.
9. Share your writing with your audience.

Helpful Hints for Writing

Knowing and using the hints below can be helpful when you revise your writing.

Capitalize these words:

- names of people and pets
    Jenny   Harold R. Smith   Sparky

- titles used with names
    Dr. Nathaniel Goode   Ms. Lynn Streit

- the word **I**
    Ann and I are going to the movies.

- days of the week and months of the year
    Sunday   January

- the first word in the greeting and closing of a letter
    Dear Louise,   Your friend,

- the first word in a sentence
    We will read for ten minutes.

Use periods:

- at the ends of statements or commands
    I have a pen in my desk.   Please pass the milk.

Use commas:

- between the day and the year in a date
  February 25, 1990

- after the greeting and closing of a friendly letter
  Dear Anastasia,   Sincerely,

Use exclamation marks:

- after sentences that show strong feeling
  What a wonderful day it is!

Use question marks:

- after sentences that ask questions
  Who erased the spelling words?

Editing Marks

EDITING MARKS

¶   indent or start a new paragraph

≡   use capital letter

◯   check spelling

∧   add letters or words

ℓ   take out

⊙   add a period

¶ Jupiter is the largest planet we know⊙ It ⟨terns⟩ _turns_ much faster than earth. A day on jupiter is only hours long. ¶ Four off Jupiter's moons can _ten_ ∧ be seen with a telescope.

    Jupiter is the largest planet we know. It turns much faster than Earth. A day on Jupiter is only ten hours long.
    Four of Jupiter's moons can be seen with a telescope.

Common Abbreviations

An abbreviation is a shortened form of a word. Abbreviations are useful in taking notes, but words should be spelled out in formal writing.

January **Jan.**	November **Nov.**	Thursday **Thurs.**
February **Feb.**	December **Dec.**	Friday **Fri.**
March **Mar.**		Saturday **Sat.**
April **Apr.**	Sunday **Sun.**	
August **Aug.**	Monday **Mon.**	quart **qt.**
September **Sept.**	Tuesday **Tues.**	seconds **sec.**
October **Oct.**	Wednesday **Wed.**	minute **min.**

Handwriting Models

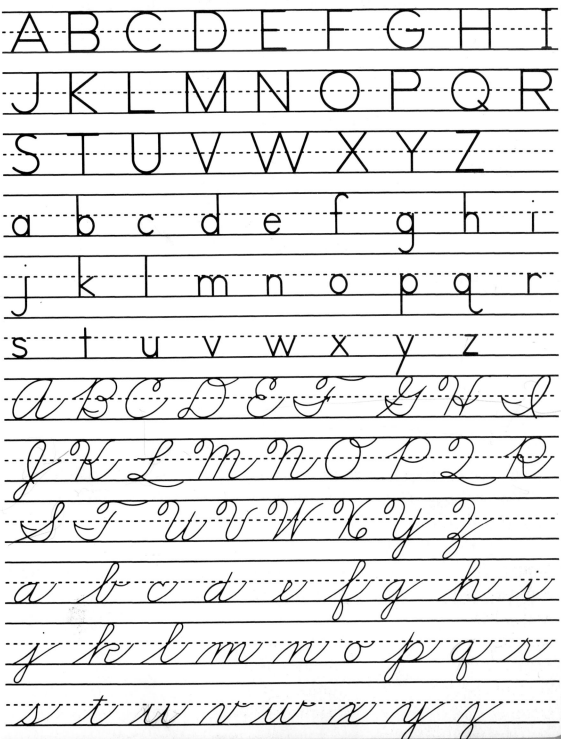

Spelling Glossary

Base Word   A base word is the simplest form or main part of a word. You can form new words by adding word endings to the ends of base words. Adding **-s** to the base word **rock** makes the new word **rocks**. **See page 41.**

Body   The body of a letter is the main part of the letter. It contains the letter's message. **See page 82.**

Closing   A closing in a letter is the word or words that are used to say good-by. The first word in the closing begins with a capital letter. A comma follows the last word. **See page 82.**

Consonant   A consonant is a letter of the alphabet that is not a vowel. Some consonants are **b, f, g, w.** **See page 10.**

Consonant Cluster   A consonant cluster is two or more consonant sounds said together and spelled with more than one letter. **Clap** has the consonant cluster **cl**, and **grew** has the consonant cluster **gr.** **See page 49.**

Definition   A definition is a meaning given for a word. Definitions can be found in dictionary entries. If there is more than one definition for a word, the definitions are numbered in the dictionary. The definition of **bit** is ''a small piece of something.'' **See page 81.**

Dictionary   A dictionary is designed to help you find the correct spelling, syllabication, pronunciation, and meaning of a word.

Double Letters   A double letter is one sound spelled with the same two letters. The word **penny** has a double **n.** The word **sheep** has double e. **See page 101.**

Editing Mark   An editing mark is a symbol used in proofreading to show where changes are needed in meaning, word order, spelling, capitalization, or punctuation.

Entry   In a dictionary, an entry is the entry word plus all the information about the word that follows. Some of the entry words under **c** in a dictionary might be **call, car,** or **chew. See page 76.**

Entry Word   An entry word in a dictionary is listed in alphabetical order, appears in bold print, and shows the correct spelling of a word. Entry words are sometimes divided into syllables to show where the word can be divided. **See page 76.**

Example Sentence   In a dictionary, an example sentence often follows a definition and helps explain the entry word. An example sentence for the word **fine** might be: **She felt fine. See page 86.**

Exclamation Mark   An exclamation mark is a punctuation mark used to end a sentence showing excitement, surprise, or strong feeling. This sentence is an exclamation: **Look out! See page 103.**

Fable   A fable is a story that teaches a lesson.

Friendly Letter   A friendly letter has five parts: heading, greeting, body, closing, and signature. **See page 82.**

Greeting   The words in a letter that tell whom it is for are called the greeting. The first word in a greeting begins with a capital letter. In a friendly letter, a comma follows the greeting. **See page 82.**

Guide Words   Guide words are the words in bold print that are placed at the top corners of each page of a dictionary. All entry words on the page are arranged alphabetically between the two guide words. Guide words are helpful in finding words quickly. **See page 66.**

Heading   The heading of a letter is found in the upper right-hand corner. It contains the date. Commas are used between the day and the year in the heading. **See page 82.**

Noun   A noun is the name of a person, place, thing, or idea. **See page 20.**

Paragraph   A paragraph is a group of sentences that tells about one main idea. It usually begins with a main idea sentence that states the main idea. All other sentences in the paragraph tell more about or support the main idea sentence. The first word in a paragraph is indented or set in from the left side. **See page 118.**

Period   A period is a punctuation mark used to end a sentence that makes a statement or gives a command.

Plural   Plural means "more than one." The plurals of most nouns are formed by adding **-s** or **-es** to the noun. The plural of **bed** is **beds**. The plural of **box** is **boxes**. **See page 20.**

Punctuation Mark   Punctuation marks are used in writing to show where sentence parts begin and end or to make sentence meanings more clear. Periods, question marks, exclamation marks, and commas are punctuation marks.

Question   A question asks about something. It is followed by a question mark. The following sentence is a question: **What time is it? See page 72.**

Question Mark   A question mark is a punctuation mark used to end a sentence that asks something. **See page 72.**

Rhyming words   Rhyming words have the same middle and ending sounds. **Men** and **pen** are rhyming words. **See page 5.**

Riddle   A riddle can be a funny question that makes you think about the meanings of words. **See page 24.**

Sentence   A sentence is a group of words that tells one complete thought. The first word in a sentence begins with a capital letter. A sentence may end with a period, question mark, or exclamation mark. **See page 5.**

Signature   In a letter, the signature appears after the closing and contains the sender's name. **See page 82.**

Thesaurus   A thesaurus is a list of words and their synonyms, or words that mean about the same thing.

Verb   A verb is a word that expresses action or state of being. **See page 51.**

Vowel   The vowels **a, e, i, o,** and **u** are important building blocks in words. Vowels connect the consonant sounds in words. Every word has at least one vowel. **See page 10.**

How to Use a Dictionary/Thesaurus

A **dictionary** helps you say a word and use it correctly.
A **thesaurus** gives synonyms for each entry word.
Guide words are found at the top of each page in a dictionary or thesaurus. The guide word on the left shows the first word on that page. The one on the right shows the last word on that page.

The word you look up is an **entry word.** Spaces are used to show how the word is divided into syllables. All entry words are in alphabetical order.

Other **forms** of the entry word are given if the spelling changes when an ending is added.

A **synonym** is a word that means the same or almost the same as the entry word.

cut   cut; cut ting 1 CHOP; to cut or break into pieces with a sharp tool: *Chris will cut the apple with a knife.* **2** to hurt the skin with something sharp: *Did Linda cut her finger on the tin can?*

A **definition** tells what the word means. Each meaning will be numbered.

An **example sentence** gives you a better understanding of how to use the word.

Spelling
Dictionary/Thesaurus

A

a bout **1** ALMOST: *He is about six years old.* **2** having something to do with: *The book is about the circus.*

add **add ed; add ing** **1** to put things together to make more: *Add some water to the soup.* **2** SUM; to put numbers together: *If you add two and two, your answer should be four.*

ad di tion *We learn addition in arithmetic class.*

af ter BEHIND; later than: *We will wash the dishes after dinner.*

air ATMOSPHERE; the gas mixture that surrounds the earth: *We don't want to pollute the air.*

al most NEARLY; only a little less than: *Kate is almost ready to go.*

a long ON: *We stopped at a bakery along the way.*

al so TOO: *Carl is also going to camp.*

al ways EVER; at all times: *Karen is always happy.*

and **1** a word used to join words: *We will sing and play.* **2** added to: *One and one make two.*

ant insect related to bees: *There was an ant on the flower.*

an y **1** one of many: *Any of you can play.* **2** some: *Do you have any money?*

a part ment ROOM; set of rooms in a building where people live: *Callie lives in an apartment.*

ap ple a round fruit that grows on a tree and often has red skin: *Tony ate an apple.*

are a form of **be**: *They are my best friends.*

arm a top part of the body between the shoulder and hand: *Sally broke her arm.*

as *Tad is as big as Dad.*

ask **asked; ask ing** QUIZ; to find out about: *They will ask the questions.*

aunt the sister of your father or mother: *Pedro's aunt is a doctor.*

B

ba by **ba bies** a very young boy or girl

ba by- sit ter one who takes care of young children or babies: *We have a great baby-sitter.*

¹**back** **1** the rear part of the body: *Mitch has a fly on his back.* **2** the place at the rear: *Dan is in the back of the house.*

²**back** **backed; back ing** REVERSE; to move back: *Back the car out of the driveway.*

bait something used to catch or trap: *The fisherman used bacon for bait.*

bake **baked; bak ing** ROAST; to cook food by putting it into a hot oven: *Bake the bread until it is light brown on top.*

ball **1** GLOBE; something round: *The kitten has a ball of string.* **2** a round toy used in games: *The children played with the red ball.*

band **1** group of musicians: *The band played at halftime.* **2** STRIP: *A skunk has a white band down its back.*

bank **1** a place that takes care of money: *Mr. Rinaldo works at the bank.* **2** a small thing like a jar used for saving money: *Grandma gives me dimes to put into my bank.*

barn a farm building where animals live and hay is kept: *The cows sleep in the barn.*

barn

base ball **1** a game played with a bat and a ball between two teams of nine players each: *Ned likes to play baseball with the other children.* **2** the ball used in this game

bas ket ball **1** a game in which each of two teams tries to get a ball into a high basket: *We play basketball after lunch.* **2** the ball used in this game

¹**bat** **1** a small animal that flies at night **2** CLUB; a heavy stick used for hitting: *He hit the ball with a bat.*

²**bat** **bat ted; bat ting** to hit: *Jim will bat the ball.*

bath WASH; a washing of the body: *I take a bath when I am dirty.*

bay a small body of water: *The water in the bay was warm.*

be am; is; are; was; were; been
be ing *Ann has to be on time tomorrow.*

beach SHORE; sand or little stones along the side of rivers, oceans, or lakes: *We go to the beach every summer.*

bear a large heavy animal with hair and a short tail: *A bear eats fruit and honey.*

be cause for the reason that: *We will go home because it is raining.*

bed CRADLE; something to lie or sleep on: *Nancy sleeps in a big bed.*

been a form of **be**: *I have never been to the circus.*

be fore AHEAD; at an earlier time: *I hope you can come before summer.*

bell something that rings when you hit it or shake it: *The teacher rang the bell after lunch.*

bend CURVE: *There is a sharp bend in the road near our house.*

bet ter EXCELLENT; more good or more right: *I feel better now that my cold is gone.*

be tween AMONG: *It was a secret between us.*

bike BICYCLE; a two-wheeled vehicle powered by pedals

bill a piece of paper money: *Ceil can pay for the milk with a dollar bill.*

bird a flying animal covered with feathers

birth day the day a person was born: *My birthday is February 6.*

¹**bit** PART; a small piece of something

²**bit** a form of **bite**; CHEWED: *I bit into an apple.*

black black er; black est the color of coal: *The truck had black wheels.*

blew past of **blow** made air move: *The wind blew the door shut.*

¹**blind** a window shade: *The blind keeps the sunlight out.*

²**blind** not able to see: *My friend is blind.*

blow blew; blown; blow ing 1 to move, often quickly and hard: *We felt the wind blow.* 2 to send out strong air from the mouth: *Can you blow out the candles?*

blue blu er; blu est the color of a clear sky: *The sky made the lake look blue.*

boat SHIP; something that sails on water

bone the hard part of an animal or person: *Bonita broke a bone in her foot.*

book VOLUME; something to read

born BIRTH; brought into the world: *The pony was born in the barn.*

both the two; the one and the other: *Mary held both her hands near the fire to warm them.*

¹**bow**   RIBBON: *Nancy always has a bow in her hair.*

²**bow**   BEND: *The dancer took a bow when she was finished.*

³**bow**   BEND: *The dancer will bow at the end.*

box   boxes   something with four sides to put things into: *Pablo put the clothes into a box.*

brave   BOLD: *She was very brave during the emergency.*

bring   brought; bring ing   TAKE; to come with something or someone from another place: *Christy will bring the books home from the library.*

broth er   a boy or man who has the same parents as another person

brown   brown er; brown est   the color of a tree trunk

¹**brush   brush es**   something used to fix hair, to paint, or to clean: *Use this brush to get the dirt off your coat.*

²**brush   brushed; brush ing**   SKIM; to fix hair, paint, or clean with a brush: *I must brush my teeth.*

bud   SEED; the beginnings of a plant: *There were buds and flowers on the rose bush.*

build   built; build ing   CONSTRUCT; to make or put together: *Cassie wants to build an airplane.*

bunch   bunch es   GROUP: *Carrie picked a bunch of wild flowers.*

bush   bush es   a low tree: *The bush has red berries.*

but ter fly   but ter flies   a flying insect with brightly colored wings: *There is a pretty butterfly in the garden.*

butterfly

buy   bought; buy ing   PURCHASE; to get something by paying money: *Susan will buy a bag of apples.*

C

cake **1** a baked food: *Karol did not want any cake after dinner.* **2** something molded or shaped together: *The cake of soap fell into the sink.*

call **called; call ing** **1** CRY: to speak in a loud voice: *Please call her to come home.* **2** to name: *I call my rabbit Pinky.* **3** to talk to by telephone: *I'll call you tonight.*

came a form of **come** **1** moved toward: *The dog came when I called.* **2** ARRIVED: *Uncle Ted came to our house yesterday.*

¹can something that holds food: *I bought a can of corn.*

²can **could** ABLE; to be able to: *You can win the race because you run so fast.*

can not UNABLE: *There cannot be a rainbow without sunlight.*

cap HAT; a small hat: *Denny has a baseball cap.*

car AUTO; something to ride in that moves on wheels

catch **caught; catch ing** CAPTURE; to grab something that is moving through the air: *Try to catch the ball when I throw it.*

caught a form of **catch**: *Marvin caught the butterfly in the net.*

cent one penny: *The button cost one cent.*

chair a seat with a back: *Nobody was sitting in the chair.*

change SWITCH; make different: *Did you change your mind?*

chase **chased; chas ing** TRAIL; to follow something in order to catch it: *The hunter will chase the rabbit.*

chew **chewed; chew ing** BITE; to use your teeth on food: *You must chew your food.*

chick a baby chicken: *The chick has soft feathers.*

chil dren YOUTHS; more than one child; young people

¹chill a feeling of cold: *I got a chill.*

²chill to cool: *Let's chill the watermelon.*

chin a part of the face under the mouth: *He has a cut on his chin.*

chop **chopped; chop ping** CARVE; to cut into small pieces: *Sam will chop the wood.*

cit y **cit ies** a large town with many buildings and people: *Boston is a city.*

clap **clapped; clap ping** BANG; to make a noise by hitting two hands together: *After the show, we will clap our hands.*

class GROUP: *We have twenty-five students in our class.*

¹clean **cleaned; clean ing** CLEANSE; to remove dirt from something: *Please clean your room.*

²**clean**   **clean er; clean est**   without dirt: *Mr. Winston has a clean house.*

cliff   a high and steep face of rock: *There was no way to climb the steep cliff.*

climb   **climbed; climb ing**   to use the hands and feet to move up or down something: *Be careful when you climb the ladder.*

clock   a machine that shows what time it is: *The clock says it is one o'clock.*

clothes   CLOTHING; coverings for the body: *These clothes are too big to fit me.*

coal   something that can be burned to make heat: *This building is heated by burning coal.*

coat   **1** a piece of clothing worn to keep warm **2** the covering on an animal

col or   SHADE: *The color I like best is blue.*

com bine   MIX: *Combine all the ingredients and blend well.*

cone   **1** a shape like a triangle: *I would love an ice cream cone.* **2** pine tree seeds: *Morgan made a pine cone wreath.*

¹**cook**   CHEF; a person whose job is to cook: *Mr. Wright is a cook at our school.*

²**cook**   **cooked; cook ing**   BAKE; to make food by heating it.

cool   COLD: *Drink the cool glass of water.*

corn   a yellow vegetable: *We bought corn at the market.*

cost   **cost; cost ing**   CHARGE; to have a price of: *The hats cost three dollars each.*

could   a form of **can**: *Jeremy could not run very far.*

cow   a large farm animal that gives milk: *The cow is eating grass in the field.*

cow

cry   **cried; cry ing**   WEEP; shed tears: *Sad movies make me cry.*

cub   **1** the young of certain animals: *The bear cub could not leave its mother.* **2** a young news reporter: *The newspaper hired two new cub reporters.*

¹**cut**   GASH; a break in the skin made by something sharp: *I fell off my bicycle and got a cut on my leg.*

²**cut**   **cut; cut ting**   **1** CHOP; to slice or break into pieces with a sharp tool: *Chris will cut the apple with a knife.* **2** to hurt the skin with something sharp: *Did Linda cut her finger on the tin can?*

cute   **cut er; cut est**   nice to look at: *What a cute little baby!*

D

dad dy   **dad dies**   FATHER: *Their daddy is a tall man.*

¹**dark**   DUSK; the time when there is no light from the sun; night: *My little sister goes to bed at dark.*

²**dark**   **dark er; dark est**   DIM; without light: *It is dark at night.*

day time   DAY; the time of daylight: *We will drive only during the daytime.*

den   **1** a resting place for wild animals: *Bears often stay in a den during cold winters.* **2** STUDY; a quiet room, often used for reading: *Dad always likes to read in the den.*

desk   a writing table: *I do my homework at a desk.*

did   a form of **do**: *Jan did her work.*

dig   **dug; dig ging**   to turn over dirt or make a hole in the ground: *Lin used a shovel to dig a place for a garden.*

din ner   FEAST; the main meal of the day: *The Rossetti family eats dinner at six o'clock.*

dish   PLATE; something on which to place food: *Mary put the dish of green beans on the table.*

do   **did; done; do ing**   *I will do the dishes.*

doc tor   PHYSICIAN; a person who helps sick people

dog   a furry animal that barks: *My dog likes to chew bones.*

doll   a toy that looks like a baby or a little child

door   GATE; a part in a wall that opens and closes: *Shut the door when you go outside.*

door way   ENTRANCE; the opening filled by a door: *The door no longer fit in the doorway.*

down   DOWNWARD; toward or to the ground; to a lower place: *Samantha fell down the hill.*

¹**dress**   **dress es**   a piece of clothing sometimes worn by women and girls

²**dress**   **dressed; dress ing**   to put on clothes: *Do you dress yourself in the morning?*

¹**drink**   BEVERAGE; something that can be drunk: *Would you like a drink of cold water?*

²**drink**   **drank; drunk; drink ing**   SIP; to swallow something such as water: *The horses will drink from the river.*

¹drop DRIP: *I felt a drop of rain.*

²drop **dropped; drop ping** to let fall: *Don't drop the dishes.*

drove **driv ing; driv en** past of **drive:** *Dillon drove all night to get home.*

dry **dri er; dri est** not wet: *The clothes will be dry after they hang on the line.*

duck a swimming bird that has a bill, a short neck, short legs, and webbed feet: *A white duck lives near the pond.*

duck

dug past of **dig:** *The dog dug a deep hole.*

E

each ALL; every one: *Each kitten is sleeping in the barn.*

ear a part of the head that is used to hear: *His ear hurt from the loud noise.*

egg **1** a kind of food: *Darla ate an egg for breakfast.* **2** something found in a bird's nest: *The hen sat on the egg until the chick hatched.*

¹eight the number following seven; 8

²eight one more than seven: *A stop sign has eight sides.*

eigh teen the number between seventeen and nineteen; 18

eighth one more after seventh: *Paul was eighth in line.*

e lec tric run by electricity: *Mary has an electric train.*

emp ty VACANT; having nothing inside: *The new house was empty until yesterday.*

end FINISH; the last point or part of something: *The end of the story is sad.*

en try ENTRANCE: *Some animals have more than one entry to their den.*

ev ery ALL; each: *Every person watched the parade.*

eye   a part of the face used to see: *The dog has one blue eye and one brown eye.*

F

face   the front part of the head

¹**fall**   the time of year between summer and winter: *Fall is a pretty time of year.*

²**fall**   **fell; fall en; fall ing**   DROP: *Apples fall from trees.*

fam i ly   **fam i lies**   a group of people who are related: *There is a new family in our neighborhood.*

far   **far ther; far thest**   DISTANT; a long way: *Claudia works far from home.*

farm   a piece of land used to grow food and on which to keep animals

fast   **fast er; fast est**   SWIFT; quick: *The morning train is fast.*

¹**fat**   a type of oily animal cell or tissue: *The doctor said I have very little fat.*

²**fat**   PLUMP: *The fat goose likes to eat corn.*

fa ther   a man who has children

feel   **felt; feel ing**   TOUCH: *I feel the grass with my hands.*

feel ing   TOUCH: *He was feeling his way in the dark.*

feet   **1** the part of the body on the end of legs, used for walking and standing: *He stood on his feet.* **2** more than one foot: *Jimmy is three feet tall.*

fell   a form of **fall**   DROPPED: *I fell out of bed last night.*

fif teen   the number between fourteen and sixteen

fifth   one more after fourth: *The fifth grade went on a field trip.*

¹**fif ty**   the number following forty-nine; 50

²**fif ty**   one more than forty-nine

fill   **1** to put into as much as can be held: *Fill your glass with milk.* **2** PLUG; to plug up holes: *A carpenter will fill the cracks.*

film   **1** HAZE; a thin layer: *The steam made a thick film on the window.* **2** a coated paper to take pictures with: *We ran out of film for our camera.* **3** MOVIE: *Cinderella was a great film.*

find   **found; find ing**   LOCATE; to look for and get: *Did you find the lost key?*

fine   very well: *She felt fine.*

fire   BLAZE; flame, heat, or light made by burning: *We cooked hot dogs over the fire.*

first the one coming in front of or before all others: *Juanita is the first in line.*

¹**fish** **fish** or **fish es** **1** an animal that swims in water **2** food from fish: *Chris ate fish for dinner.*

²**fish** **fished; fish ing** to catch or try to catch fish

floor the part of a room on which people stand: *Joe mopped the kitchen floor.*

flow er BLOSSOM; the part of a plant with pretty colors: *A flower can be red, pink, yellow, or orange.*

¹**fly** **flies** a small insect with wings

²**fly** **flew; flown; fly ing** FLOAT; to move through the air: *Look at the birds fly.*

fly ing SKIMMING; moving through the air: *Those birds are flying south for the winter.*

foot **feet** **1** the end of the leg on which a person stands: *The shoe is too big for my foot.* **2** twelve inches (about 30 cm): *I need a piece of string that is a foot long.*

for *The present is for Uncle Wilson.*

for got a form of **forget** failed to remember: *Michael forgot that it was my birthday.*

found a form of **find** DISCOVERED: *They found treasure in the old ship.*

¹**four** the number after three; 4

²**four** QUARTET; one more than three

free LOOSE; not contained: *The pony was free in the barnyard.*

friend PAL; a person you know and like: *Camille is my friend.*

frog a small green animal that hops: *A frog lives in our pond.*

frog

from out of: *Jim is from the city*

full **full er; full est** **1** COMPLETE; filled all the way: *The glass is full of water.* **2** having a lot: *The bush is full of bugs.*

fun PLAY; a good time: *They had fun at camp.*

fun ny **fun ni er; fun ni est** LAUGHABLE: *The clown was doing funny tricks.*

fur HIDE; the coat of hair on animals

G

gate   DOORWAY; way to get in and out of a door or fence: *Please close the gate.*

gave   a form of **give** OFFERED: *My father gave us a ride.*

get   got; got ten; get ting   1 to receive: *Everyone will get a turn.* **2** to become: *I get hungry at lunch time.*

girl   a young woman: *I met a girl named Mary Jane.*

glad   glad der; glad dest   CHEERFUL; happy or pleased: *The neighbors were glad to meet you.*

goat   an animal like a sheep with horns: *The goat likes to play in the yard.*

gold   a yellow metal often used to make jewelry: *He wears a gold ring.*

gone   a form of **go** WENT: *We have gone to the lake many times.*

good   bet ter; best   1 NICE; happy: *Have a good time at the fair.* **2** not bad: *Joe is a good singer.* **3** RIGHT: *It was good of you to return the lost money.*

goose   geese   a large bird that has a long neck and looks like a duck

goose

got   a form of **get**: *I got your letter.*

grain   1 food from cereal plants **2** BIT; very little: *There was only a grain of salt left.*

gram   a weight (about .035 ounce): *A big paper clip weighs about one gram.*

grand chil dren   children of one's own son or daughter: *All of my grandchildren have brown eyes.*

grass   grass es   the green covering on yards and fields: *The girls cut our grass every Saturday.*

great   great er; great est   1 IMPORTANT: *Susan B. Anthony was a great woman.* **2** very good: *We had a great time at camp.*

grew a form of **grow** RAISED: *Tim grew five inches taller this year.*

grow **grew; grown; grow ing** to become bigger: *Your rose bush will grow fast there.*

H

hail small ice clumps that fall from the sky like rain during a storm: *We went inside when hail started to fall.*

hand the end part of the arm used for holding and picking up things: *Teddy has a cup in his hand.*

hap py **hap pi er; hap pi est** CHEERFUL; glad or pleased: *I am happy you are here.*

hard **hard er; hard est** **1** not easy: *Some words are hard to spell.* **2** SOLID; not soft: *The bread is as hard as a rock.*

has a form of **have** **1** to own: *Pat has red hair.* **2** MUST: *Nat has to finish his book today.*

hat CAP; a covering for the head: *My hat keeps my ears warm.*

have **had; hav ing** **1** OWN: *Gail and Bob have old sleds.* **2** MUST: *I have to stay in today.*

hay cut, dry grass used as food for animals

head the top part of the body where the face is: *David has a cap on his head.*

heard a form of **hear** LISTENED: *Michael heard the music.*

¹**heat** WARMTH: *The heat from the fire warmed us.*

²**heat** to make warm: *Please heat this food for dinner.*

¹**her** a word used in place of a girl's name or a woman's name: *Kim is hungry, so give the apple to her.*

²**her** belonging to a woman or a girl: *Ann had her book.*

hide **hid; hid den; hid ing** CONCEAL; to get where no one can see you: *Dan will hide behind the tree.*

hill a high piece of ground: *There is a hill behind our house.*

¹**hit** baseball hit: *She got one hit during the game.*

²**hit** STRIKE: *She will hit the ball very hard.*

hog PIG: *Wilbur was a make-believe hog.*

hog

hole   GAP; an opening or a deep place: *My pocket has a hole in it.*

hop   **hopped; hop ping**   **1** SKIP; to move by taking small jumps **2** to jump on one foot: *Can you hop to the door?*

hope   **hoped; hopes; hop ing**   WISH; wanting something to happen: *I hope it snows.*

horse   a large animal used for working and riding: *Grandma let us ride the horse on the farm.*

hot   **hot ter; hot test**   HEATED; very warm: *It is a hot day.*

house   SHELTER; a building where people can live: *The Farnums live in a brick house.*

how   in what way: *How can you walk so fast?*

hun dred   the number 100

hunt   **hunt ed; hunt ing**   SEARCH; to go after animals for food or fun: *In the country, some people hunt for food.*

hurt   **hurt; hurt ing**   HARM: *Don't hurt the kitten.*

I

ice   water made hard by freezing: *When it is cold, the water in the pond turns to ice.*

if   *We can't have a picnic if it rains.*

in   AT: *Ken put the frog in a box.*

inch   **inch es**   one of twelve equal parts of a foot (about 2.5 cm): *The baby's finger is an inch long.*

itch   a feeling that makes one want to scratch: *Chicken pox may give you an itch.*

J

jet   an airplane that flies using a jet motor: *A jet flies very fast.*

joke   **joked; jokes; jok ing**   a very short, funny story: *I heard that joke yesterday.*

K

keep   **kept; keep ing**   HOLD; to save: *The teacher will keep our papers.*

¹kid   a young goat: *The kid ate all of our roses.*

²kid   JOKE: *Don't kid about that.*

¹kind   a group or part of a group: *The kind of fruit I like best is oranges.*

²kind   **kind er; kind est**   NICE; good: *Mr. Gibbs is a kind man.*

king dom   a land ruled by a king or queen: *Everyone in the kingdom loved the queen.*

kite   a toy that is covered with paper or cloth and flies in the air: *My kite is flying into those branches.*

kit ten   a baby cat: *The kitten played with a ball of string.*

knew   a form of **know**: *I knew they would come late.*

knock   **1** POUND: *Knock on the door.* **2** MOVE: *Don't knock that lamp over!*

know   **knew; known; know ing**   UNDERSTAND: *The boys know how to skate.*

L

lake   a large body of water with land around it: *We went swimming in the lake.*

lamb   a baby sheep: *The lamb has soft wool.*

¹**land**   EARTH: *America was a new land.*

²**land**   come to earth: *When did the plane land?*

lane   **1** a narrow path or road: *Let's walk down the lane.* **2** bowling lane: *They like to bowl in lane one.*

large   **larg er; larg est**   GREAT; big: *The box was so large that it would not fit through the door.*

last   FINAL; coming after all others: *Tony is the last one in line.*

left   the opposite side of right: *Joan writes with her left hand.*

leg   part of the body used for walking: *She hurt her leg in the race.*

let   **let; let ting**   PERMIT; to allow: *Mom will let me have an apple.*

li brar y   **li brar ies**   a building or room where books are kept: *Our class is going to the library.*

¹**light**   **1** something to see by: *Turn on the light so the room is not so dark.* **2** DAYLIGHT; something that shines from the sun: *I wake up when the morning light comes through my window.*

¹**light** (definition 1)

²**light**   **light ed** or **lit; light ing**   to make something give off light or to start a fire: *Be careful when you light the candle.*

³**light**   **light er; light est**   **1** pale in color; not dark: *My shirt is light blue.* **2** not heavy: *Because it was light, my balloon blew away in the wind.*

line   **1** a piece of rope, string, or wire: *Please hang the clothes on a line.* **2** ROW; a row of things or people: *They are waiting in line for the show.* **3** a straight mark: *Sam drew a line on his paper.*

lips   the part of the mouth outside the body: *I can hide my lips.*

lit tle   **lit tler; lit tlest**   **1**   TINY; small in size: *The kitten is little.* **2** not much: *There is a little milk left.*

live   **lived; liv ing**   **1** to stay in a place: *Does Kate live in that house?* **2** ALIVE: *People, animals, and plants grow and change while they live.*

¹**load**   BURDEN; what someone is carrying: *Chris is pulling a heavy load of rocks.*

²**load**   **load ed; load ing**   to put something onto something else to carry it: *Help me load the hay onto the wagon.*

log   long thick part of a cut tree, usually the trunk: *We need more logs for the fire.*

long   **long er; long est**   **1** LENGTHY; not short: *Her hair is so long, it reaches the middle of her back.* **2** from beginning to end: *This story is twelve pages long.*

look   **looked; look ing**   **1** SEE: *I look at the stars every night.* **2** to hunt for: *He will look for the puppy's collar.* **3** to seem or appear: *Your mittens look just like mine.*

lot   **1** a piece of land: *We will build a house on that lot.* **2** GROUP; a large number of things: *Ms. Carter has a lot to do.*

lot (definition 1)

low   **low er; low est**   **1** not high or tall: *The baby sits in a low chair.* **2** not loud; soft: *He spoke in a low whisper.*

luck   FORTUNE; a chance that something will happen: *Julia went fishing, but she didn't have any luck catching fish.*

M

make   made; mak ing   FORM; to put together: *We will make a kite.*

man   men   a grown-up boy: *That man is my father.*

man y   SEVERAL; a large number of: *There are many people in the circus tent.*

map   CHART; a sketch to show some feature of a place: *I use a map to help me travel.*

mask   a cover for the face: *The doctor wore a mask.*

¹match   match es   a short, thin stick used to light a fire

²match   matched; match ing   1 to go well together: *These two red gloves match each other.* **2** AGREE; to put things together so that they go well with each other: *Jim likes to match his tie with his suit.*

may   might   1 to allow: *You may go to the circus.* **2** to be possible: *We may have a storm tonight.*

meat   FOOD; a food that comes from animals: *Do you eat meat for dinner?*

meet   met; meet ing   GREET; to come together: *We will meet them at the corner.*

men   more than one man: *One woman and two men are standing in line.*

mend   REPAIR; FIX: *Grace will mend that tear tonight.*

mile   5,280 feet (about 1.6 km): *I walk a mile every day.*

milk   a white drink that comes from cows

mill   FACTORY; a building with machines that make corn or wheat into flour: *There is a mill near the farm.*

mill

¹mind   BRAIN; the part of a person that knows, thinks, and feels: *You use your mind whenever you're awake.*

²mind   mind ed; mind ing   1 WATCH; to look after: *Kara will mind the children while we are gone.* **2** to not like: *Do you mind if I leave early?*

¹mine   a pit that has coal or gold in it: *The men went down into the mine.*

²mine   my own: *This book is mine.*

min ute   MOMENT; short time; sixty seconds: *An hour is sixty times longer than a minute.*

¹Miss   a young girl or woman: *Our teacher is Miss Gray.*

²miss   missed; miss ing   1 to want to be with someone: *I miss Kim.*
2 to not hit or not catch: *Will Nat miss his bus?*

mo ment   INSTANT; very short time: *A blink only takes a moment.*

mon ey   CASH; something used to buy and pay for things

month   one of the twelve sections of a year: *January is the first month of the year.*

moose   an animal like a very large deer: *A moose lives where it is cold.*

¹mop   a tool used to clean floors with soap and water: *I cleaned the spilled milk off the floor with a mop.*

²mop   mopped; mop ping   to clean by using a mop: *Please mop this dirty floor.*

more   ADDED: *Can you eat more vegetables?*

morn ing   DAWN; the early part of a day; before noon: *I eat breakfast every morning.*

most ly   MAINLY; for the most part: *Today will be mostly cloudy.*

moth   a flying insect something like a butterfly: *The moth was attracted to the light.*

moth er   a woman who has children: *My mother is a bus driver.*

move   moved; mov ing   1 to change the place of something: *Please move the box to the floor.*
2 SHIFT; to go from one place to another

much   more; most   *We did so much work.*

mud   SOIL; soft, wet dirt:

mu sic   a pleasing sound: *Father plays beautiful music on the piano.*

must   SHOULD: *Andrew must wash the dishes tonight.*

N

¹nail   1 something used to hold pieces of wood together
2 something that grows on a finger or toe

²nail   nailed; nail ing   to put pieces of wood together by hitting a nail with a hammer

need   need ed; need ing   WANT: *The kittens need food.*

nest   a home made by a bird for its eggs and young: *There is a bird's nest in our apple tree.*

nev er   not ever: *Ramon has never missed a day of school.*

new   new er; new est   FRESH; not old: *Carlo has a new toy.*

news   REPORT; things that just happened: *Mom always watches the six o'clock news.*

¹next   NEAREST; coming before or after: *They live in the next house.*

²next   AFTER; in the nearest time or place: *Open this box next.*

nice   **nic er; nic est**   PLEASING: *Your new coat is nice.*

night   NIGHTTIME; the last part of the day when it is dark

none   NOBODY; not any: *None of them are going to the show.*

not   *Matt is not going.*

now   TODAY; at this time: *Can you help me now?*

num ber   *Twelve is a number.*

O

o cean   SEA; large area of salt water: *The ocean is very wide.*

of   having: *She bought a bag of popcorn.*

off   **1** not on: *Please turn off the water.* **2** away from: *Jose fell off the step.*

oh   a word that shows surprise: *Oh! I didn't know you were here.*

old   **old er; old est**   **1** not new: *My shoes are old.* **2** AGED; not young: *My uncle is old.*

¹on   working: *The television set is on.*

²on   AT; against or upon: *His hat is on the chair.*

on ly   ALONE; one and no more: *She is the only girl on the team.*

on to   to a point on: *The cat climbed onto the roof.*

¹o pen   **o pened; o pen ing**   to change from shut: *Will you open your books?*

²open   not shut: *The window is open.*

or   *Are you leaving now or later?*

oth er   DIFFERENT; the one left: *This coat keeps me warmer than my other coat.*

our   belonging to us: *Jackie would like to see our piano.*

o ver   **1** ABOVE: *The birds flew over our heads.* **2** ACROSS: *Try to jump over the puddle.* **3** DONE; at an end: *The show is over at eight.*

P

paid   form of **pay**   gave money: *Patty paid for my lunch.*

pair   COUPLE; a set of two things that go together

pal ace   a large home for royalty: *The palace was always open to visitors from the kingdom.*

pa rade   DISPLAY; a show in which people march: *There is a parade in many cities in November.*

par rot   a colorful bird: *Ben's parrot can talk.*

¹**part**   PIECE: *Part of the paper is wet.*

²**part**   **part ed; part ing**   SEPARATE; to leave: *It is time for us to part.*

par ty   **par ties**   a group of people together having a good time: *Our friends are having a party on Saturday.*

peek   GLANCE; look quickly: *Babies like to peek at you.*

¹**peep**   CHIRP; the sound a baby chick makes: *The chick would make a peep when it was hungry.*

²**peep**   PEEK; LOOK: *He tried to peep through a knothole in the fence.*

pen ny   **pen nies**   a cent: *I have a shiny new penny.*

peo ple   girls, boys, men, and women: *I like to watch the people go by.*

pick   **picked; pick ing**   SELECT; to choose or gather: *Lorna is going to pick some flowers.*

pie   PASTRY: *Bart makes good apple pie.*

piece   PORTION; a part of something: *Throw a piece of bread to the ducks.*

¹**pin**   a piece of metal used to hold things together: *She used a pin on her doll's coat.*

²**pin**   FASTEN; JOIN: *You need to pin the top of your shirt.*

pink   **pink er; pink est**   a pale red color: *The inside of the rabbit's ear was pink.*

¹**plant**   something that grows from a seed, is often green, and sometimes has flowers: *This plant will grow well in our garden.*

²**plant**   **plant ed; plant ing**   SOW; to put a seed or plant in dirt so it will grow: *Plant the rose near the front door.*

¹**plant**

¹**play**   a story acted by people: *Our school put on a play.*

²**play**   **played; play ing**   AMUSE; to do something just for fun: *Children love to play.*

¹**please**   **pleased; pleas ing**   DELIGHT; to make someone happy: *This picture will please my teacher.*

²**please**   if you will: *Please pass the salt.*

plus   ADDED: *Four plus one is five.*

pond   a small body of water with land around it: *The ducks are swimming in the pond.*

pot   **1** a deep pan used for cooking food: *There is chicken soup in the pot on the stove.* **2** a deep bowl in which plants or flowers grow: *James filled the pot with dirt and planted a flower in it.*

pret ty   **pret ti er; pret ti est** BEAUTIFUL; nice to look at: *The picture is very pretty.*

prince   male member of a royal family: *The prince was soon to become king.*

prin cess   female member of a royal family: *The princess was the youngest member of the royal family.*

prob lem   QUESTION: *A little thought solved the problem.*

pull   **pulled; pull ing**   DRAG; to move something toward you without picking it up: *Help me pull the wagon up the hill.*

pup py   **pup pies**   PUP; a baby dog

put   **put; put ting**   to place or move a thing somewhere: *Put your toys in the box.*

Q

quart   a measure of liquid amounts: *Chrissie bought a quart of milk.*

R

ra di o   *We hear the news on our radio.*

rain   drops of water that fall from the sky

read   **read; read ing**   to understand the meaning of words written on a page: *The children read the books at home.*

reed   **1** a type of tall grass with slender stems **2** a wooden strip used on some musical instruments: *He placed a new reed on his clarinet.*

rich   **rich er; rich est**   WEALTHY; having a lot of something: *The rich queen gave away some money.*

right   the opposite of left: *John writes with his right hand.*

¹**ring**   a band to wear around a finger: *Becky wears a pretty gold ring on her right hand.*

²**ring** **rang; rung; ring ing**   CHIME; to make a sound that is like the sound of a bell: *Did you hear the telephone ring?*

road   WAY; a street: *This is a bumpy road.*

rob **robbed; rob bing**   STEAL; to take something that doesn't belong to the one taking it: *We hope no one will rob the store.*

¹**rock**   a large stone

²**rock** **rocked; rock ing**   SHAKE; to move back and forth or from side to side: *Jeff will rock the baby to sleep.*

room   **1** a part of a house: *Maxine is sleeping in her room.* **2** SPACE: *There is no room for him to sit.*

rug   a cloth that covers a floor: *I took off my muddy shoes before I walked on the rug.*

S

safe **saf er; saf est**   free from danger: *Birds lay their eggs in safe places.*

said   a form of **say**: *Rita said she would visit us soon.*

sale   something sold at a lower price: *The grocery store had a sale on peaches.*

same   ALIKE: *The twins wear the same type of clothing.*

same

sand   GRIT; tiny grains of rock on a beach or shore: *We made a castle out of sand.*

¹**saw**   a tool for cutting wood

²**saw**   to cut something with a saw

³**saw**   a form of **see**   LOOKED; used the eyes to look at someone or something

say **said; say ing**   TELL; to speak: *What did she say?*

sea   OCEAN; a large body of salt water that covers much of the earth: *Ships sail on the sea.*

¹**seat**   a place or a thing to sit on: *There is one empty seat on the bus.*

²**seat** **seat ed; seat ing**   help someone find a place to sit: *John will seat the baby in the high chair.*

sec ond   MOMENT; the 60th part of a minute: *A minute is sixty times longer than a second.*

see   **saw; seen; see ing**   VIEW; to use the eyes to look at someone or something: *Can you see the boat on the lake?*

seed   the beginnings of a plant: *This large pumpkin grew from a small seed.*

send   **sent; send ing**   SHIP; to make someone or something go from one place to another: *We can send Bud to the store to buy flour.*

sense   FEELING; body awareness of the world: *The sense of sight is one of the five senses.*

sent   a form of **send**   made someone or something go from one place to another: *Larry sent a birthday card to his mother.*

¹set   GROUP; people or things that belong together: *Mother has a beautiful set of art books.*

²set   **set; set ting**   SETTLE; to put down: *Set the box here.*

shall   WILL: *I shall be glad to help.*

¹shape   FIGURE: *The shape of a square has four equal sides.*

²shape   FORM: *I can shape clay to make a car.*

she   that female: *She is going to school.*

sheep   **sheep**   a farm animal with a warm coat

shin y   BRIGHT; catching light: *I scrubbed the pot until it was shiny.*

shirt   a piece of clothing worn on the upper part of the body: *We gave Mother a new shirt.*

shoe   a covering for a foot: *Tie your shoe.*

¹shop   STORE: *Let's go to the pet shop.*

²shop   **shopped; shop ping**   to look in stores: *We are going to shop for new shoes.*

shore   COAST; the land around a body of water; beach: *A large sea bird is walking along the shore.*

short   **short er; short est**   LOW; not tall: *Mannie is a short girl.*

¹shot   something to help someone who is sick get well: *Dr. Ross gave me a shot in my arm.*

²shot   a form of **shoot**   *The fire fighters shot water through the windows of the burning building.*

should   OUGHT: *You should whisper in the library.*

¹show   a story on the radio or television: *We will watch a good show this morning.*

²show   **showed; shown; show ing**   **1**   PRESENT; to let someone see: *Show your picture to the teacher.* **2** to teach: *Pat will show him how to dance.*

sick   **sick er; sick est**   ILL; not well: *Kevin stayed home from school because he was sick.*

side   **1** the right or the left part of a person or thing: *That side of the house is painted red.*

sigh   MOAN; to make a sound while taking a deep breath: *She will sigh when she sees this mess.*

sil ly   **sil li er; sil li est**   **1** FUNNY; *Dan was being silly when he barked like a dog.* **2** FOOLISH; not wise: *It was silly of me to lock the keys in the car.*

sing   **sang; sung; sing ing**   to make pretty sounds using the voice: *The people can sing the songs.*

sis ter   a girl or woman who has the same parents as another person: *My sister is older than I am.*

sit   **sat; sit ting**   to rest on a chair or the floor: *Come and sit by me.*

sixth   the one after fifth: *Paul was the sixth person in line.*

six ty   the number after fifty-nine and before sixty-one

size   how much: *My sister and I wear the same size boots.*

sky   **skies**   the air over us: *Look at the bird in the sky!*

¹sled   a large toy to sit on and slide down a hill: *This sled goes fast over snow.*

²sled   **sled ded; sled ding**   to slide quickly on snow: *I will sled down this hill.*

sleep   **slept; sleep ing**   NAP; to rest with closed eyes: *Pam will sleep at my house tonight.*

slid   form of **slide**   *She slid into second base.*

¹slide   a large toy in the shape of a hill that children can slide down while sitting: *There is a slide near the swings at the park.*

²slide   **slid; slid ing**   SLIP; to move quickly or easily: *The skater will slide across the ice.*

slip   **slipped; slip ping**   **1** to move quickly or easily: *Slip this dime into your pocket.* **2** SKID; to slide and fall: *Don't slip on the ice.*

snail   a small animal that has a shell and moves slowly: *We found a snail on the beach.*

snail

snake   a reptile with no arms or legs: *A black snake helps farmers.*

so da   **1** a sweet drink: *The cooler was filled with cold soda.* **2** a type of chemical mixture: *Cooks use soda in baking.*

soft   **soft er; soft est**   **1** GENTLE; not hard: *The snow is soft and fluffy.* **2** not loud: *Rob talked in such a soft voice that I could not hear him.*

soft ball   a game like baseball, but one in which a larger ball is used: *Those children all play softball.*

softball

some   a number of: *I saw some lions at the zoo.*

sound   NOISE; anything that can be heard: *The sound of barking dogs woke me up.*

¹**spot**   a small mark: *There is a spot of dirt on his tie.*

²**spot**   **spot ted; spot ting**   to see or find: *Ralph can spot the deer in the woods.*

stand   **stood; stand ing**   to be upright on the feet: *We will stand when the principal comes.*

start   **start ed; start ing**   **1** BEGIN: *Did the game start late?* **2** to turn on: *The car will not start.*

¹**state**   one of the units of a nation: *Alaska is a state in the United States.*

²**state**   SAY: *Please state what is on your mind.*

stay   **stayed; stay ing**   REMAIN; to stop at a place: *We will stay at Grandma's.*

stem   the main part of a plant that holds the leaves and buds: *No leaves grew on the bottom of the stem.*

step   **1** FOOTPRINT; a move by putting one foot in front of the other: *Tim took a giant step.* **2** a part of stairs

step fa ther   the husband of one's mother by a later marriage: *My stepfather took me to a baseball game.*

stick   TWIG; a broken branch of a tree or bush: *Give me the stick.*

¹**still**   **still er; still est**   **1** CALM; without moving: *You must sit still.* **2** without noise; very quiet: *The room became very still.*

²**still**   YET; up to this or that time: *Are you still here?*

sting   **stung; sting ing**   a sharp, small hurt: *Did that bee sting you?*

stone   ROCK: *There is a stone in my shoe.*

¹**store**   MARKET; a place where things are sold: *Buy fruit at the store.*

²**store**   **stored; stor ing**   to put something away for later use: *The chipmunks store food for winter.*

sto ry   **sto ries**   REPORT; something to read or tell: *He told us a true story about fishing.*

¹**stuff**   **1** a bunch of things: *Put this stuff in a box.* **2** MATERIAL; what something is made from: *I need lots of stuff to make that pie.*

²**stuff**   **stuffed; stuff ing**   PACK; to push things into something: *He had to stuff the clothes into a box.*

sub tract   **sub tract ed; sub tract ing**   DEDUCT; to take away: *When you subtract three from ten, you have seven.*

sub trac tion   *We learn subtraction in arithmetic class.*

such   so great: *Have you ever seen such tall buildings before?*

suit   a set of clothes that match: *Grandpa is wearing a blue suit.*

sum   TOTAL; the answer to an addition problem: *The sum of six and six is twelve.*

sun light   SUNSHINE; the light of the sun: *There will be few clouds and a lot of sunlight tomorrow.*

swim   **swam; swum; swim ming**   to move through the water by using the arms and legs: *Marta can swim across the pond.*

¹**swing**   a seat that hangs from ropes or chains: *Grandpa tied a swing to the old oak tree.*

²**swing**   **swung; swing ing**   WAVE; to move back and forth, often in the air: *The monkeys swing from the tree branches.*

T

¹**tag**   **1** MARKER: *Dad put a tag on his hammer to label it.* **2** GAME: *Most children enjoy playing tag.*

²**tag**   **1** LABEL: *Please tag all of your belongings.* **2** TOUCH: *Run fast and tag your friend.*

take   **took; tak en; tak ing**   **1** GRAB; to carry: *Carolyn can take the books to the library.* **2** to choose: *I'll take the green apple, and you can have the red one.* **3** to need: *This job will take a lot of time.*

¹talk SPEECH: *Dr. Edwards gave a talk on animals.*

²talk talked; talk ing DISCUSS; to use words to speak

taste tast ed; tast ing get the flavor of something by putting it in the mouth: *Did you taste the pizza?*

teach taught; teach ing TRAIN; to help someone learn how to do something: *Clara can teach us to make paper airplanes.*

teach er COACH; a person who shows someone how to do something: *Mr. Golding is a very good spelling teacher.*

teeth plural of **tooth** hard mouth parts used for chewing food: *Sarah brushes her teeth every day.*

tel e vi sion *We saw a show about lions on television.*

tell told; tell ing SAY: *Tell me your name.*

tent SHELTER: *We always use a tent when we go camping.*

tenth one more after ninth: *It is the tenth day of the month.*

than in comparing: *My brother is older than I am.*

thank thanked; thank ing to say or show you are pleased: *I will thank Father for the present.*

the that one: *The last one out should lock the door.*

their belonging to them: *They left their muddy boots outside.*

then **1** at that time: *I lived on a farm back then.* **2** NEXT: *I'll dry the dishes and then go play.*

there at a place: *We will swim in the lake when we get there.*

these the ones here: *These are my new shoes.*

thing OBJECT; that which can be seen, touched, heard, tasted, or smelled: *What is that red thing in your hand?*

think thought; think ing IMAGINE; to have ideas: *Can you think of a way to fix the broken toy?*

third after the second: *This is the third time we have seen that show.*

¹thir ty the number following twenty-nine; 30

²thir ty one more than twenty-nine

this these the one here: *This story is long.*

those plural of **that** the kinds: *Are those bananas ripe?*

¹thought IDEA: *That's a happy thought!*

²thought a form of **think** *Jack thought about what he had read.*

¹**tie**   BAND; a long piece of cloth worn around the neck: *Mr. Pang has a new tie and suit.*

²**tie**   **tied; ty ing**   to make a knot: *Watch me tie my shoes.*

till   UNTIL: *I didn't turn the television on till after dinner.*

time   **1** OCCASION; when something happens: *This is a good time to play.* **2** the minute, hour, day, or year as seen on a clock or calendar

toad   amphibian with no tail and rough, dry, warty skin: *A toad lives mostly on land.*

to day   this day: *The sun is shining today.*

toe   the end part of a foot: *He hurt his big toe.*

ton   a way to measure very heavy things: *A ton is two thousand pounds.*

too   **1** ALSO: *Ms. Ying is going, too.* **2** more than enough: *I ate too much.*

took   a form of **take**   **1** CARRIED **2** CHOSE **3** NEEDED

top   **1** a toy that spins **2** PEAK; the highest point: *We walked to the top of the hill.*

tore   a form of **tear:**   *Terry tore her new suit.*

touch   FEEL: *I don't want to touch that snake.*

town   a place with buildings and houses, smaller than a city: *The name of our town is Somerville.*

¹**train**   a line of railroad cars: *This train can carry cows and coal.*

¹**train**

²**train**   **trained; train ing**   TEACH: *She will train her cat to do tricks.*

¹**trap**   TRICK; a thing that catches something or someone: *In that board game, Rose fell into my trap.*

²**trap**   CATCH: *How many did you trap in Hide and Seek?*

¹**trick**   a thing that fools people: *The clown did a card trick.*

²**trick**   **tricked; trick ing**   to fool people: *Kim likes to trick me.*

truck   a large car that can carry large or heavy loads: *The movers put tables, chairs, and beds into the truck.*

true   **tru er; tru est**   REAL; correct; full of truth: *I like true stories because they tell about things that have really happened.*

trunk   **1** an elephant's nose **2** a box or chest for storing things **3** the main part of a tree

tub   BATHTUB: *We have a new tub in our bathroom.*

¹**turn**   CHANGE: *It is your turn at bat.*

²**turn**   TWIST: *Please turn the volume down.*

¹**twen ty**   the number following nineteen; 20

²**twen ty**   one more than nineteen

¹**two**   the number after one; 2

²**two**   one more than one

U

un der   BELOW: *The dog is hiding under the chair.*

us   *The bus will take us to camp.*

¹**use**   BENEFIT: *What's the use of crying?*

²**use**   **used; us ing**   *May I use your bicycle?*

V

vil lage   a group of houses and streets, smaller than a town: *I saw a little village in the country.*

W

wa ges   SALARY; payment for work: *We will earn wages for mowing the lawn.*

wag on   a cart with four wheels often used to carry things: *Let's put all the toys into his wagon.*

wake   **waked** or **woke; waked** or **wo ken; wak ing**   to stop sleeping: *I always wake when the sun comes up.*

¹**walk**   a trip that is taken by walking: *We took a walk around the block.*

²**walk**   **walked; walk ing**   PACE; to move along on one's feet: *The baby has just learned to walk.*

want   **want ed; want ing**   DESIRE; to need or to wish for: *I want to go to the circus.*

warm **warm er; warm est** HOT; in between hot and cold: *There are many warm days during the spring.*

wash **washed; wash ing** to clean with water: *Wash your hands before you eat.*

¹**watch** **watch es** a small clock worn on the arm: *Ask Tina what time is on her watch.*

²**watch** **watched; watch ing** to look for or look at carefully: *Watch out for cars when you cross the street.*

¹**wa ter** *Sea water is salty.*

²**water** **wa tered; wa ter ing** to put water on: *I water the plants in the evening.*

watering

¹**wave** a moving curve of water: *The wave hit the beach.*

²**wave** SWING; move something back and forth: *Did you wave your hand?*

weath er what it is like outside; wet or dry, hot or cold, etc.: *What is the weather like today?*

weed a plant growing where it isn't wanted: *We need to pull that weed.*

¹**well** a deep hole filled with water: *We will drop a penny into the well.*

²**well** **bet ter; best** NICELY; good: *Our play went well.*

went a form of **go**: *The calf went with its mother.*

were form of **be**: *You were right to wear your raincoat.*

wet **wet ter; wet test** DAMP; not dry: *Hang the wet clothes on the line.*

what which thing: *What is the answer?*

wheel something round that helps a car, bicycle, or wagon to move

when which time: *When should we come?*

when ev er any time: *I wear gloves whenever it snows.*

where **1** to what place: *Where did Dave go?* **2** at that place: *Stay where you are.*

which what one or ones: *Which of the three books is yours?*

¹**while** a short time: *You can stay for a while.*

²**while** during the time that: *Susan can sleep while I get washed.*

¹**whis tle** **1** something that makes a loud, high sound when air blows through it: *The basketball game ended when the teacher blew a whistle.* **2** the sound made by a whistle: *The dog's ears stood up when it heard a whistle.*

²**whistle** **whis tled; whis tling** to make a high sound by blowing air through a whistle or between the lips. *When I feel happy, I sometimes whistle a song.*

who what or which person or persons: *Who broke my cup?*

whole ALL: *Our family ate the whole pie.*

why REASON: *He told us why he was late.*

wide BROAD: *The lake covers a wide area.*

will *They will come soon.*

win **won; win ning** GET; be the best in the contest: *What did you win?*

win

win ter the time of the year between fall and spring: *Where I live, it snows in winter.*

wire a thin metal string: *The wire fence kept the dog in the yard.*

¹**wish** **wish es** DESIRE; something wished for: *Blow the candles out and make a wish.*

²**wish** **wished; wish ing** WANT; to long for or want: *My brothers wish they could go to camp.*

with **1** *We will go with you.* **2** *She painted the picture with a brush.*

wood the hard part of a tree: *They made the house from wood.*

¹**work** a job: *Farming is hard work.*

²**work** **worked; work ing** to do a job: *They work in the fields.*

would *Everybody would like to meet the new neighbors.*

write **wrote; writ ten; writ ing** to make letters or words with pen or pencil: *I can write my name.*

wrong **1** FALSE; not right or correct: *The answer is wrong.* **2** bad: *Taking things that belong to others is wrong.*

wrote a form of **write:** *Andy wrote two letters today.*

Y

yard **1** three feet (about .9 m): *I need one yard of cloth to make the skirt.* **2** the land around a house: *Dad planted a garden in the front yard.*

yel low **yel low er; yel low est** the color of the sun: *Paint the flower bright yellow.*

you the one or ones being talked to: *I will tell you when to begin.*